It's Another Ace Book from CGP

This book is for 9-10 year olds.

Classbooks 5A and 5B cover the shiny new Numeracy
Strategy for year five at school.

They're brilliant fun. That makes them great classbooks —
and fantastic books to use with kids at home.

Homework book 5 follows on from the classbooks with loads of
extra-juicy questions to get brains bulging and marks rising.

CGP are just the best

The central aim of Coordination Group Publications is to produce
top quality books that are carefully written, immaculately
presented and marvellously funny — whilst always making sure they
exactly cover the National Curriculum for each subject.

And then we supply them to as many people as we possibly can,
as _cheaply_ as we possibly can.

Buy our books — they're ace

Where to Find What

These Classbooks have been carefully tailored to exactly follow the order of teaching suggested in the National Numeracy Strategy for teaching maths. Of course, this means that each topic is split into bite-size units.
To make it easier to find what you want, we've grouped them together here under the five main strands.

CALCULATIONS

NUMBERS AND THE NUMBER SYSTEM

Published by Coordination Group Publications Ltd.

Co-edited by:
Glenn Rogers BSc (Hons) and Tim Wakeling BA(Hons)

Written and Illustrated by:
Chris Dennett BSc (Hons)
Tim Major
Laura Schibrowski BSc (Hons)
James Paul Wallis BEng (Hons)
Dominic Hall BSc (Hons)

With thanks to Claire Thompson
for the Numeracy Strategy Research.

ISBN 1-84 146-056-7

Groovy website: www.cgpbooks.co.uk

Printed by Elanders Hindson, Newcastle upon Tyne.
Clipart sources: CorelDRAW and VECTOR.
1299

Money & Decimals on Calculators

Money Sums using Calculators

Fill in the calculator buttons that you need to press to work out the following sums. Then write in the answers.

This is dead easy — just write in each number and operation in order, and remember to put in the <u>decimal points</u>.

£2.54 + £9.67 = ...

When you write in the answer remember to put in the pound sign.

£6.99 – £4.59 = ...

If the answer ends with one number after the decimal, fill in the nought when you write your answer.

Harder Sums with Calculators

Use a calculator to solve these problems:

Fill in the missing number in the sum below.

Write out the sum you need to do here. Now use your calculator to work it out.

5.27 – .... = 1.68

....

The all-new *Raddehc* baseball bats had a slight design fault. <u>One</u> in every <u>three</u> bats had been made out of cheese.

1086 were made. How many have the fault?

....

Write out the sum and the answer.

Jim is saving up for his very own rollerblading horse that costs <u>£156</u>. He saves <u>£1.50</u> a week.

How many weeks will it take him to get all the money for the horse?

Reverse the sum to check the answer.

....

Check your answer.

....

Basic Shapes

Properties and Measurements of Rectangles

B

A   C

D

Draw the two diagonals on this rectangle.

Measure the length of each side and write in the results below.

Side A = ... mm   Side C = ... mm

Side B = ... mm   Side D = ... mm

All four corners have an angle of 90°. An angle of 90° is called a ....

Say why each of the shapes below is NOT a rectangle.

....

....

....

....

Rex Tangle
and the Magic Rules

....

....

Three Magic rules for Rectangles

bisect means that they <u>cross</u> at exactly <u>halfway</u>.

Choose the right words from underneath to fill in these rules about rectangles.

All four angles are	Opposite sides are .... and	**All diagonals bisect one another.**

right   equal   angles   parallel

Broken ship muddle — ship wreck tangle...

Learn all three of the magic rules for rectangles. Diagonals bisecting each other basically means when you join up diagonally opposite corners the lines cross over. See page 7 for more.

Basic Shapes

Different Types of Triangle

Measure the lengths of the sides and the sizes of the angles of all the triangles below. Write on all the measurements you make.

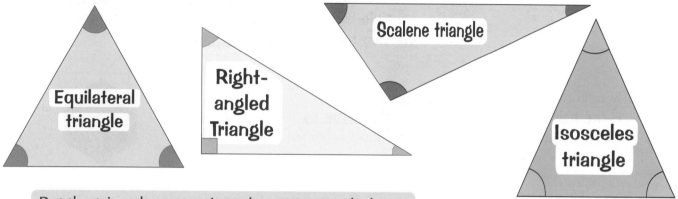

Equilateral triangle

Right-angled Triangle

Scalene triangle

Isosceles triangle

Put the triangle names into the sentences below.

An .... triangle has two equal sides and two angles the same.

In a .... triangle one of the angles is a right angle.

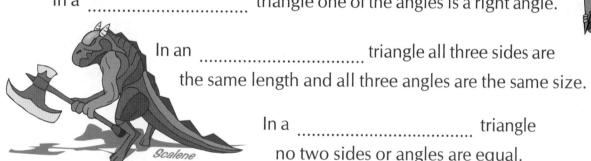

In an .... triangle all three sides are the same length and all three angles are the same size.

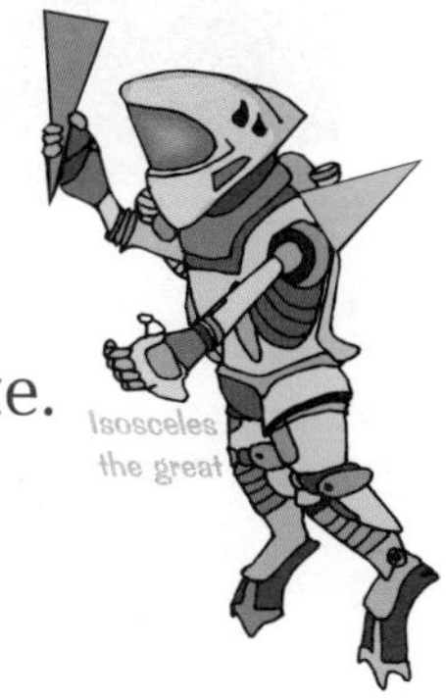

Isosceles the great

In a .... triangle no two sides or angles are equal.

Scalene the invincible

A bank has been robbed and a <u>triangular hole</u> was found in the wall. All the sides of the hole were exactly the <u>same length</u>. The usual suspects have been rounded up, but they won't talk.

Fill in all of their triangle names and then circle the one you think robbed the bank.

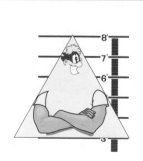
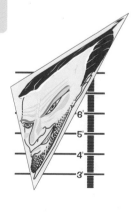
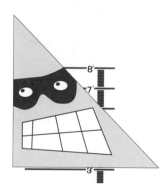

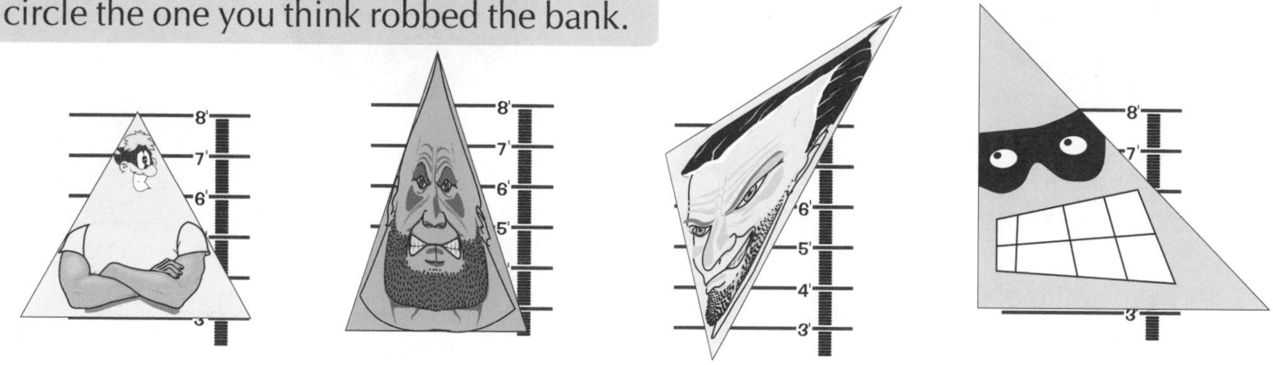

.... triangle.   .... triangle.   .... triangle.   .... triangle.

4

Symmetry in Polygons

Finding Lines of Reflective Symmetry in Polygons

There are two main ways to find the <u>lines of symmetry</u> of a shape:

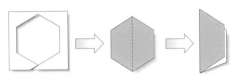

The first way is to <u>cut out</u> the shape, and <u>fold it</u> down a possible line of symmetry. If it is a line of symmetry, the two halves will <u>match exactly</u>.

The second way is to put a <u>mirror</u> on the line of symmetry. If the half shape in the mirror is <u>the same as</u> the half shape behind the mirror you've have found a line of symmetry.

Use the mirror method to draw the lines of symmetry on these irregular polygons.

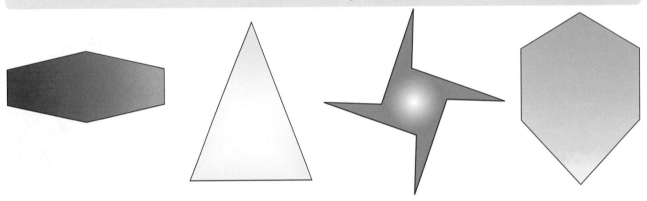

Trace these shapes onto a blank piece of paper. Use the folding method to find all their lines of symmetry. Draw on the lines of symmetry below.

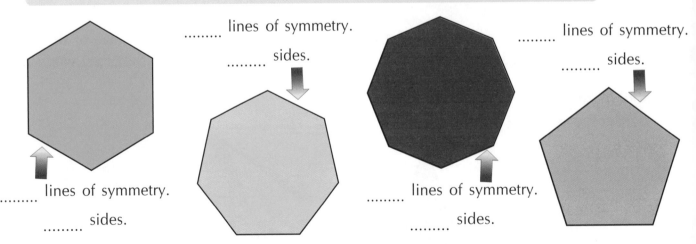

.... lines of symmetry.

.... sides.

.... lines of symmetry.

.... sides.

.... lines of symmetry.

.... sides.

.... lines of symmetry.

.... sides.

Fill in the lines beneath each shape. Write a rule about the number of sides and the number of lines of symmetry for regular polygons.

....

Symmetrical Patterns

This can get tricky, so don't rush it or you'll bodge it up.

Completing Patterns with Two lines of Symmetry

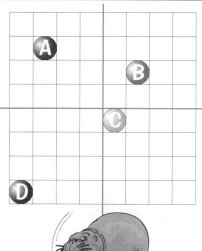

Here we have some squared paper with two lines of symmetry. To complete the pattern all the circles have to be reflected in both lines of symmetry.

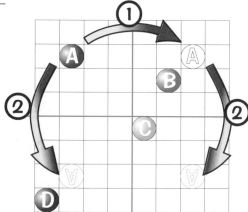

Take each circle in turn. Find its reflection in one of the lines of symmetry by counting the number of squares up to the blue line.

Now reflect both A circles in the other line of symmetry.

A and B have been done, but it's up to you to do C and D.

Once you have finished, put a mirror on the lines of symmetry to check they're all correct.

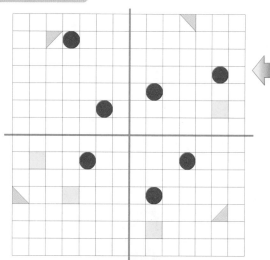

Complete these symmetrical patterns in the same way. Use a mirror to check each one.

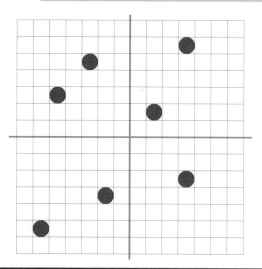

This one is very tricky.

Symmetrical Patterns — ƨnɿɘɈɈɒꟼ lɒɔiɿɈɘmmγƧ

The trick to doing these is to take each part of the pattern in turn and check that you've reflected it in all the lines. You also have to make sure you reflect the reflected bits — phew!

Parallel and Perpendicular

Definitions of Parallel and Perpendicular lines

PARALLEL lines are the same distance apart all the way along.

PERPENDICULAR lines are at right angles to each other.

Finding Parallel lines

Use the edge of a ruler to check both lines are straight.

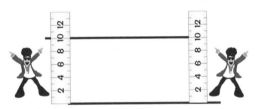

Measure the <u>shortest distance</u> from one line to the other at <u>two different</u> places. If the distance is the same the lines are <u>parallel</u>.

Finding Perpendicular lines

① <u>Extend</u> the lines so that they <u>cross</u> over.

② Then use a <u>set square</u> to judge the angle.

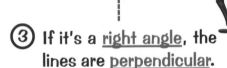

③ If it's a <u>right angle</u>, the lines are <u>perpendicular</u>.

Write under each set of lines whether they are parallel, perpendicular or neither.

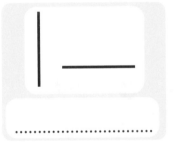

....

....

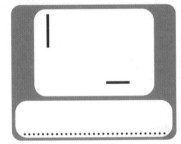

....

....

Write down the parallel sides of this square and the perpendicular sides of this octagon:

Parallel sides of a square

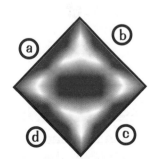

.... & ....

.... & ....

Perpendicular sides of an octagon

.... & .... & ....

.... & .... & ....

.... & .... & ....

.... & .... & ....

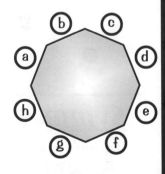

Diagonals

Definition of a Diagonal

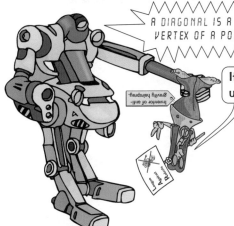

A DIAGONAL IS A STRAIGHT LINE DRAWN FROM A VERTEX OF A POLYGON TO A NON-ADJACENT VERTEX.

It's trying to say that a diagonal joins up two corners that aren't already joined.

The two <u>red lines</u> here are the only <u>diagonals</u> in a rectangle.

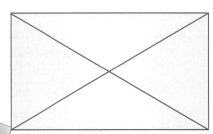

With the <u>perimeter lines</u> and the <u>diagonals</u> drawn in, all the corners should be directly connected to each other.

Finding Diagonals in Regular Polygons

Draw all the diagonals on these regular polygons, and then fill in the information below them.

HINT: Do each corner in turn — and make sure it is connected to every corner with a <u>straight line</u>.

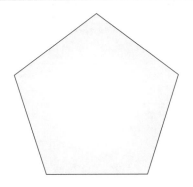

Number of sides = ...

Number of diagonals = ...

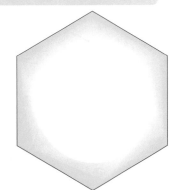

Number of sides = ...

Number of diagonals = ...

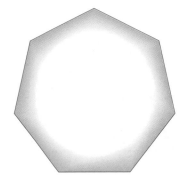

Number of sides = ...

Number of diagonals = ...

Tessa the tortoise lost the pattern on her shell. Draw on all the diagonals to give her a new pattern.

Fill in the information below.

Tessa's shell has .... sides

and .... diagonals.

Measures, Shape and Space

Acute and Obtuse Angles

Identifying Acute, Obtuse and Right Angles

Angles less than 180° are acute, obtuse, or right angles. You don't find out about angles bigger than 180° until year six — I bet you can't wait.

Fill in the blanks below with either 90° or 180°.

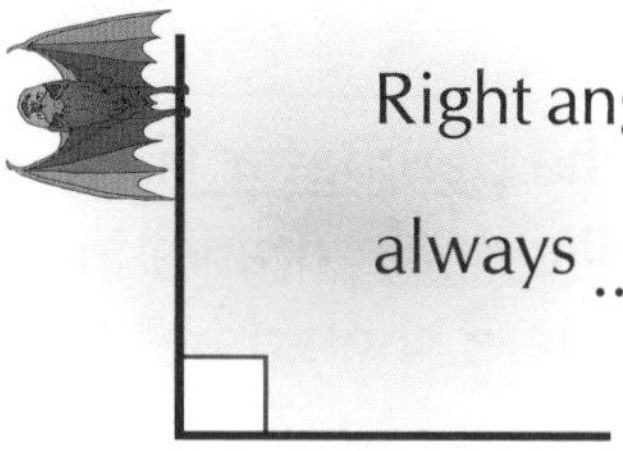

Right angles are always ....°

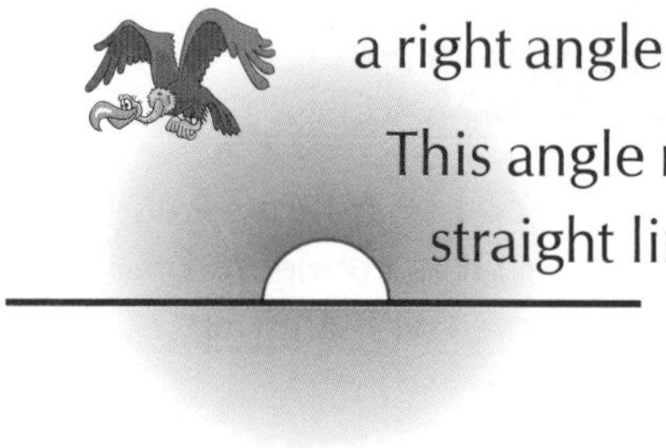

An angle twice the size of a right angle is ....°. This angle makes a straight line.

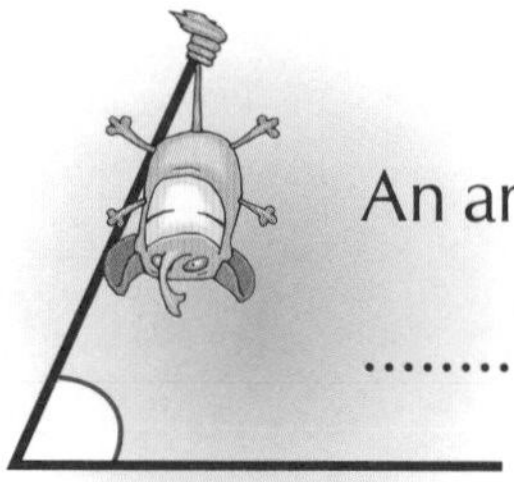

An angle less than ....° is acute.

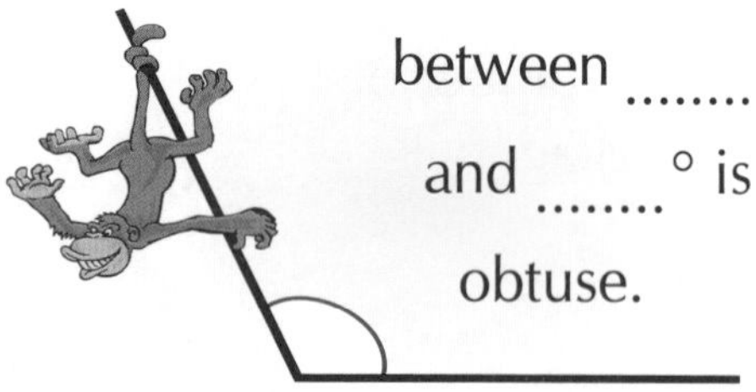

An angle between ....° and ....° is obtuse.

Write beneath each of these angles whether they are acute, obtuse or right angles.

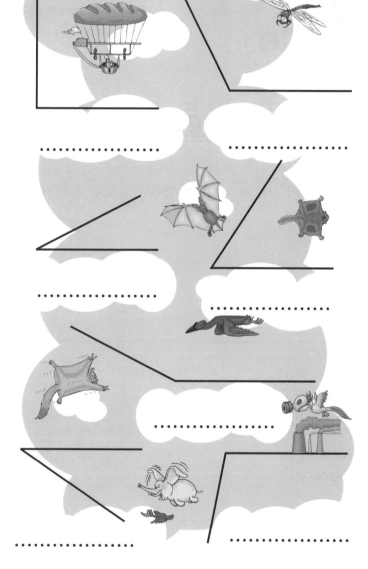

Draw a match in each picture to show;
a) a right angle;
b) an obtuse angle; and
c) an acute angle.

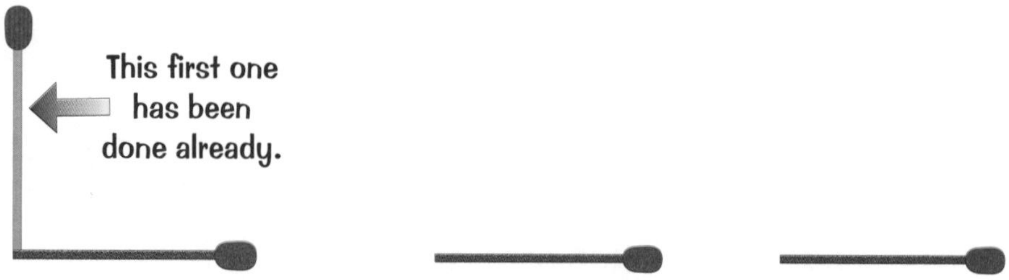

This first one has been done already.

a) right angle b) obtuse angle c) acute angle

Reasoning about Shapes

Solving Problems

Finding Shapes Within Shapes

Count all the possible rectangles in this picture.

This isn't hard, but you can easily lose count. Just plan your attack and follow the steps.

Steps:

1) Work out all the possible rectangles there could be.
2) Count the number of each type of rectangle and write it down.
3) Add up all the numbers to get your total.

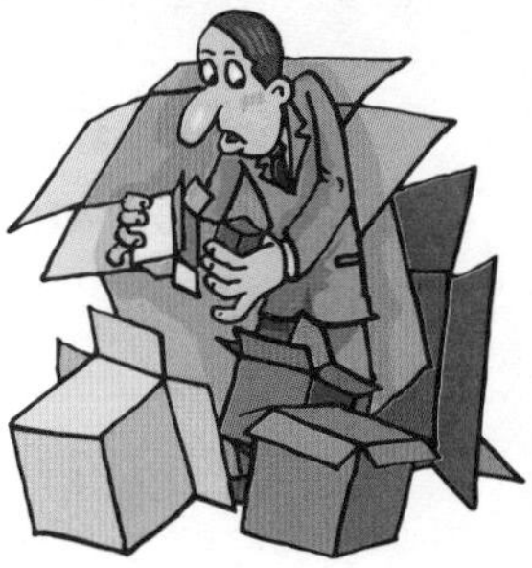

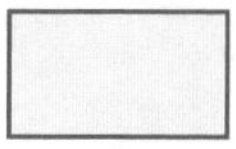 = ...
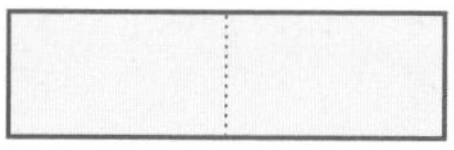 = ...
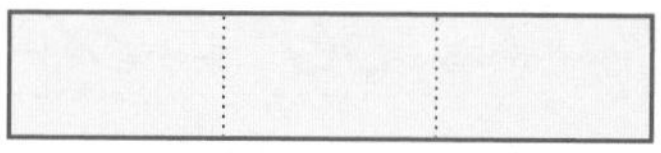 = ...

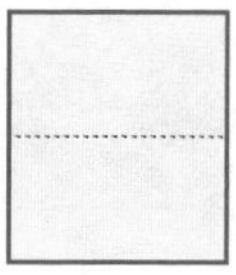 = ...
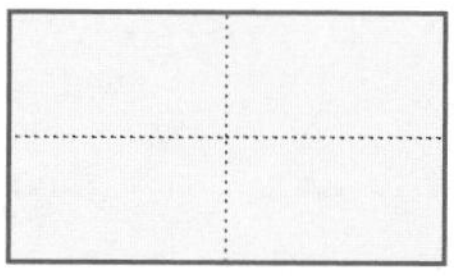 = ...
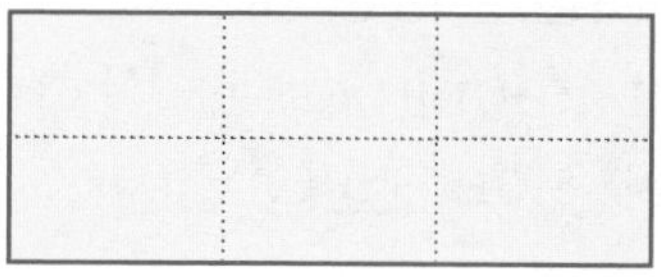 = ...

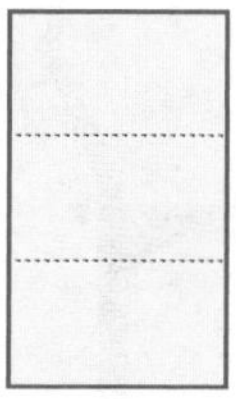 = ...
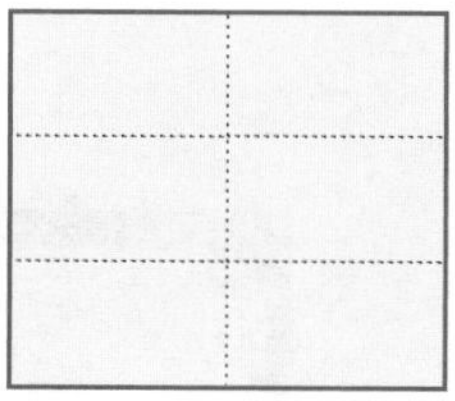 = ...
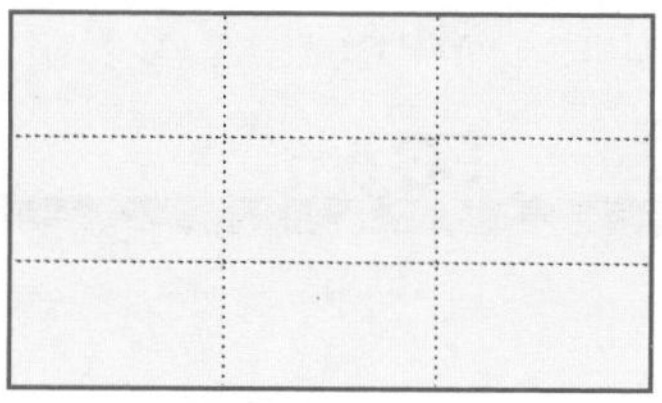 = ...

TOTAL = ...

Count all the triangles in this picture.

Now you're on your own with this one. Look at the method above to help you.

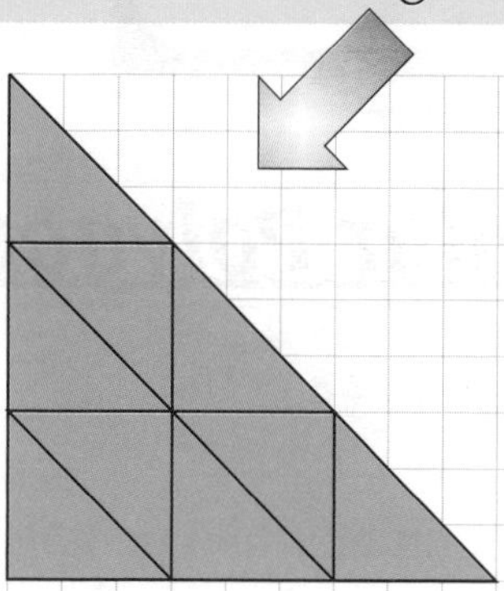

TOTAL = ...

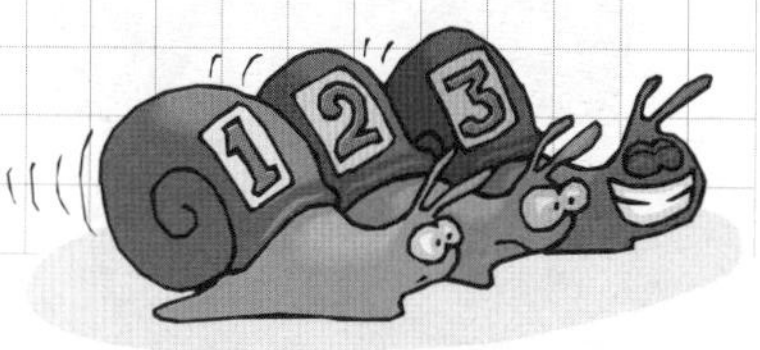

Perimeter Formulas

Formulas are just sets of instructions to help you work things out quickly and simply.

Working out the Perimeter of a Rectangle

To get the perimeter of a rectangle we add up the lengths of all the sides.

Because the two long sides of a rectangle are the same length and the two short sides are the same length we can say:

2 long sides plus 2 short sides = the perimeter of a rectangle.

$$2 \times \underline{28} + 2 \times \underline{15}$$
$$= \underline{56} + \underline{30} = \underline{86\,cm}$$

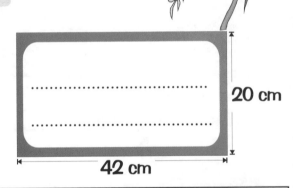

15 cm

28 cm

What is the perimeter of a rectangle if its long side is 20 cm and its short side is 5 cm?

$2 \times \ldots + 2 \times \ldots$

$= \ldots + \ldots = \ldots$

Work out the perimeters of the rectangles below.

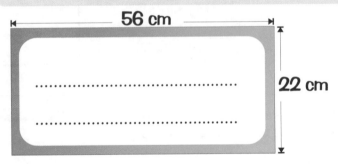

56 cm

22 cm

....

....

20 cm

42 cm

Working out the Perimeter of a Regular Polygon

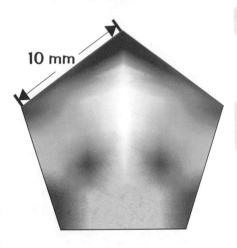

10 mm

Complete this formula for the perimeter of a pentagon.

The length of a side $\times$ .... = the perimeter of a pentagon.

Make up a formula for working out the perimeter of any regular polygon.

THIS ISN'T AS SCARY AS IT SOUNDS.

....

....

It should be similar to the one above, but it shouldn't have any numbers in it.

Measuring Area

To measure area we use square millimetres (mm²), square centimetres (cm²) or square metres (m²). The number of 1 mm by 1 mm squares that fit in a shape is its area in mm².

Measuring Area in mm², cm², and m²

Instead of counting up the squares you can find out the area of a rectangular shape by multiplying the perpendicular sides.

This square has an area of 1 cm² because each side is 1 cm long.

$$1\,cm \times 1\,cm = 1\,cm^2$$

This square has an area of 4 cm². It is made up of four 1 cm² squares.

$$2\,cm \times 2\,cm = 4\,cm^2$$

This rectangle has an area of 6 cm². It is made up of six 1 cm² squares.

$$2\,cm \times 3\,cm = 6\,cm^2$$

Work out the areas of the rectangles below.

Multiply the sides to get the area.
Make sure you get the units right (mm², cm² or m²).

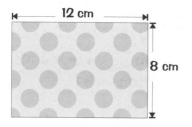

12 cm

8 cm

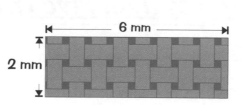

6 mm

2 mm

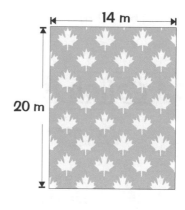

14 m

20 m

....

Write in whether you would use mm², cm² or m² when measuring the areas of these.

A car park ....   A shirt button ....

This page ....   The side of a brick ....

A fingernail ....   The top of a calculator ....

A tennis court ....   A caterpillar's rucksack ....

A birthday card ....   The floor in the classroom ....

Understanding Units and Scales

A Pint is a bit more than Half a Litre

Pints measure liquids, but they aren't used that often any more.

They are still used for delivered milk, beer in pubs and blood in hospitals.

One PINT is a bit more than half a litre — about 570 ml.

Work out these conversions using 1 pint = 570 ml.

10 pints = ... ml

3 pints = ... ml

1140 ml = ... pints

A Mile is a bit more than One and a Half Kilometres

Work out these conversions using 1 mile = 1600 m

2 miles = ... m

$\frac{1}{2}$ mile = ... m

16 000 m = ... miles

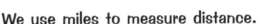

We use miles to measure distance.

Miles are used for things to do with travelling. "It's 30 miles to London" "My car goes 50 miles an hour" etc.

One MILE is a bit more than one and a half kilometres — about 1600 m.

A Gallon is a bit less than Five Litres

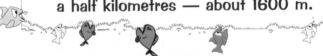

We use GALLONS to measure liquid. We still use gallons for petrol and for large quantities of water.

One GALLON is a bit less than five litres.

Work out these conversions using 1 gallon = 5 l.

4 gallons = ... l

10 gallons = ... l

200 litres = ... gallons

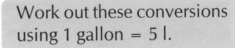

The Average Monster has 15 pints of blood. How much is this in millilitres?

.... ml

Understanding Units and Scales

Reading Measuring Scales Between Numbers

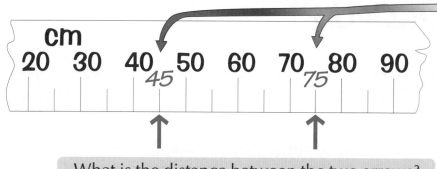

cm

20 30 40 *45* 50 60 70 *75* 80 90

The first thing to do when faced with a question like this is to write the numbers on the ruler.

Once you've done that you just have to work out the distance between them.

What is the distance between the two arrows?

75 – 45 = 30cm

What are the distances between the arrows below?

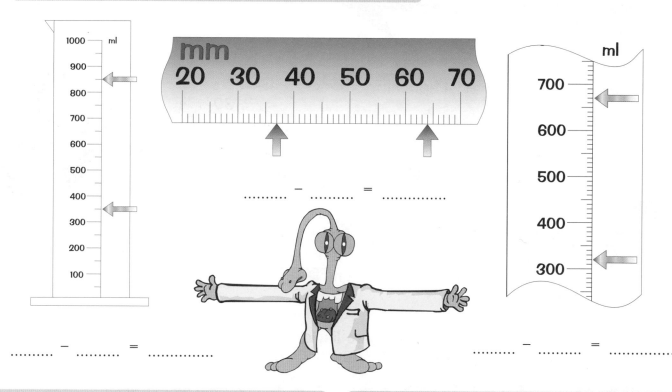

.... – .... = ...

.... – .... = ...

.... – .... = ...

If Nigel drinks 200 ml of gunk from the beaker below how much gunk will be left?

If 250 grams of green goo is taken off the scales how much green goo will be left?

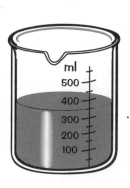

.... – .... = ...

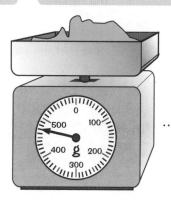

.... – .... = ...

Measures, Shape and Space

Time and the 24-Hour Clock

24-hour clocks don't stop at 12 when they get to midday, oh no, they just carry on to 13, 14 and so on up until 24. <u>Any time less than 12 is 'am'</u>. <u>Any time more than 12 is 'pm'</u>.

Reading 24-Hour Clocks

In the morning a <u>24-hour clock</u> is no different except it has a zero at the front. So <u>9:45</u> is <u>09:45</u> and can scare no one.

Things change when we get past <u>12</u> <u>noon</u>. Instead of going to <u>1 pm</u>, a 24-hour clock goes on to <u>13:00</u>.

By gum, It's two thirty in the afternoon.

To change this into 24-hour clock time, just add 12 to the hours and leave the minutes the same.

Written out as **2:30 pm** **14:30**

Change these times into 24 hour clock times.

Six thirty in the evening ➡ *6:30 pm* ➡ *18:30*

Six thirty in the morning ➡ .... ➡ ....

Five fifteen in the evening ➡ .... ➡ ....

Eleven twenty-nine at night ➡ .... ➡ ....

Change these times from 24-hour clock times to am/pm times.

If the hour number is 13 or more, take off 12 to give you the am/pm time:

17:24 = *5.24 pm* ⬅ Take away 12 from 17 to get 5. The minutes always stay the same. 23:11 = ...

07:04 = ... ⬅ Just take off the zero and add the am. 03:58 = ...

22:41 = ... 00:51 = ...

Conan knows that at 9.23 pm he must put his gas mask on. What time is this on a 24-hour clock?

....

Timetables

Knowing the 24-hour clock will help here — Look back at page 14 if you're not sure.

Using Train Timetables

The difficult thing here is keeping track of where you are in that grid of numbers. It's a good idea to lightly circle (in pencil) the numbers important to the question you're on.

DOG CITY	09:20	10:05	11.15	13.30
DUGONG	09:40	10:45	11.30	13.55
GOAT-IN-FURNESS	10:00	------	11.45	14.30
LLAMA TOWN	10:10	11:35	------	14.40
KAKAPOTON	11:25	12:55	------	16.00
FLEA-UPON-TWEED	11:55	14:15	13.25	16.45
CAT TOWN	12:30	14:55	14.00	17.25

The top line shows you all the times trains leave Dog City.

Each column gives the times for a journey and shows where and when the train stops along the way.

Some of the boxes have dashes instead of times. These are places where the train doesn't stop.

Rub out your pencil marks after each question.

Use the timetable above to answer these questions.

What time does the 09:20 from Dog City arrive at Cat Town? ....

Which is the fastest train from Dog City to Cat Town? ....

How many stations does the 11:15 from Dog City stop at before it reaches Cat Town? ....

How long does it take the 11:35 from Llama Town to reach Flea-upon-Tweed? ....

Otto's train was delayed due to invisible ants on the track. He eventually got in to Dugong at 11:22. What train should he take to get to Kakapoton?

The little blighters are everywhere.

The .... from Dugong.

Sage chairs & thyme tables — herbaceous dude...

All those numbers get a little confusing so use a pencil to circle the bits you need — but make sure you rub out the lines before you start the next question.

Handling Data	**_Probability Scales_**

Probability Shows How Likely Things Are

You <u>probably</u> use all the words on this page every day when you want to say how <u>likely</u> things are to happen.

An event is <u>likely</u> if you think it <u>will</u> happen. You can say it is <u>likely</u> to rain at <u>some point</u> this year, for example.

Something is <u>unlikely</u> if you <u>don't</u> think it will happen. It is <u>unlikely</u> that it will rain <u>every</u> day this year.

It's likely that I'll fall off!

If you are <u>sure</u> that something will happen, you can say that it is <u>certain</u>. You can be <u>certain</u> that it will get dark tonight.

If you know that an event <u>won't</u> happen, it is <u>impossible</u>. It is <u>impossible</u> for you to jump to the moon.

> Say whether these things are likely, unlikely, certain or impossible.

The name of the day tomorrow has a letter 'y' in it: ....

It will snow in July: ....

You could beat an ant in a 100 m race: ....

There is a dinosaur under your teacher's desk: ....

As well as saying whether things are <u>likely or not</u>, if we want we can say <u>how likely</u> they are. We do this by saying if there is a <u>good</u> or <u>poor</u> chance of them happening.

> Join each balloon to the person in the right place on the line.

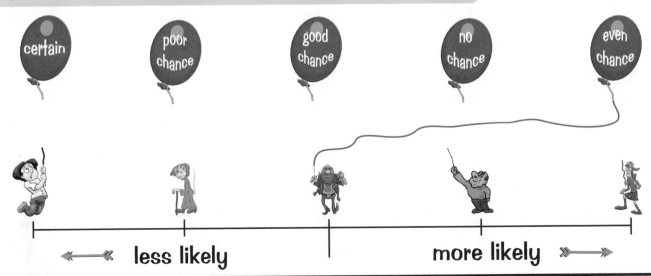

less likely   more likely

Using Data to Check Results

Check Predictions — It could be Right or Wrong

If you make a guess (or prediction) about how likely something is to happen, you can check your prediction by collecting data from an experiment.

Neil thinks that he is more likely to roll even numbers than odd numbers with a dice.

Check his prediction by rolling a dice 50 times and recording in the table how many times each number is rolled.

Number	Tally	Frequency
1		
2		
3		
4		
5		
6		

Number of odd numbers rolled = ...

Number of even numbers rolled = ...

Does your data agree with Neil's prediction? ....

If you did the experiment again, do you think you would get the same result? Explain your answer.

....

....

When data is represented in a graph it can be a lot easier to find out information from it.

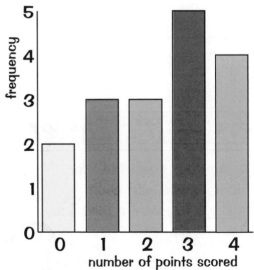

This graph shows how many points Lenny scored in a series of games with his pet tortoise.

You can find out how many games Lenny played just by counting up. There were 2 games where he scored 0, 3 games where he scored 1, and so on.

How many games did Lenny play?

....

The mode is just the number of points that occurred most often.

What was the mode of Lenny's scores? ....

In how many games did Lenny score 2 or more?

....

Mental Strategies for + and –

Looking for Pairs that Add Up to 10

Sums with 10s in them are loads easier (and a bit less scary) than those without. If you can, it helps to try and find bits of a sum that add up to 10.

EXAMPLE: What is 16 + 28 + 24?

This sum's pretty hard, but look for the bit of the sum which adds up to a number with a 0 at the end.

16 + 28 + 24

The 6 and the 4 add up to 10, so add these two first.

Once you've done that little bit, the new sum is:

40 + 28 = 68

And there we have it — easy.

Try these sums by first finding pairs that add up to 10.

15 + 18 + 25 = ... + *18* = ...

39 + 21 + 45 = ... + ... = ...

13 + 22 + 8 = ... + ... = ...

Start off with the Big Numbers — it's Easier

Don't worry if there aren't any pairs that add up to 10. Another good trick for making nasty sums easier is to start with the biggest number and add each number onto that in turn. That means that you're less likely to make a mistake.

Now do these sums by starting off with the largest number.

20 + 14 + 65 = *65* + *20* + *14* = *85* + *14* = *99*

23 + 54 + 25 = ... + ... + ... = ... + ... = ...

16 + 9 + 90 = ... + ... + ... = ... + ... = ...

7 + 22 + 88 = ... + ... + ... = ... + ... = ...

Mental Strategies for + and –

Relationships Between + and –

For any <u>addition</u> sum you can think of, there is always a <u>subtraction</u> you can make out of the <u>same numbers</u>. And you can make an addition sum from any subtraction sum.

EXAMPLE:

$$465 + 135 = 600$$

So we also know that $135 + 465 = 600$

and $600 - 135 = 465$

and $600 - 465 = 135$

Just rearrange the bits.

257 + 364 = 621.
Write 3 other statements from this sum.

....

....

....

Now that you've got that sorted, you can do <u>lots</u> of different sums from just <u>one</u> piece of information.

624 + 164 = 788. Write down the answers to these questions as fast as you can.

788 – 164 = ...

788 – 624 = ...

164 + 624 = ...

Must go faster...

Use the numbers 356, 81, 456, 437, 275, 100 and 256 to write as many addition and subtraction statements as you can.

356 – 100 = 256

....

....

....

Calculations

Mental Strategies for + and −

Making a Multiplication out of an Addition

Nobody likes adding lots of <u>big numbers</u> together.
Luckily there are sometimes <u>really neat</u> ways of doing it <u>quickly</u>.

If all the numbers are <u>close</u> to one value, then you
might be able to <u>change</u> the sum into a <u>multiplication</u>.

EXAMPLE: What is 18 + 19 + 20 + 21 + 22?

This sum looks really nasty at first, but the numbers are all close to 20.

Both of these numbers are 1 away from 20 — they "balance".

$$18 + 19 + 20 + 21 + 22$$

Both of these numbers are 2 away from 20 — they "balance" as well.

The numbers 19 and 21 are balanced because 19 is <u>one less</u> than
20, and 21 is <u>one more</u> than 20, so the extra bits <u>cancel out</u>.

Because each number is balanced by another number to make a
multiple of 20, we can say that this sum is the same as

$$20 + 20 + 20 + 20 + 20 \quad = \quad 20 \times 5 \quad = \quad 100$$

Find a multiplication that is the same as each of these sums, and then solve it.

29 + 30 + 31 = ... × ___3___ = ...

36 + 40 + 44 = ... × .... = ...

40 + 41 + 39 = ... × .... = ...

10 + 6 + 12 + 14 + 8 = ... × .... = ...

Turning + to × — now that's magic...

Make sure you can spot when you can make a long sum into a multiplication — it'll save
you a lot of time if you can. If the answer looks wrong, add the numbers up to check it.

Column Sums with Big Numbers

Adding and Subtracting Really Big Numbers

Adding big numbers is just the <u>same as normal</u> — it just takes a little bit <u>longer</u>, that's all.

Add up these numbers. Don't forget to carry if you need to.

```
    4234              1828              6729
+    326           + 2246           + 3199
```

....

The same goes for <u>subtraction</u> of big numbers — just take your time.

EXAMPLE: Work out 3826 – 1888 using the compensation method.

```
   3826
 – 1888
   1826
 +  112
   1938
```

1888 is close to 2000 so first do the
approximate sum 3826 – 2000. This
gives you 1826.

Now add back the difference between
2000 and 1888: 2000 – 1888 = 112

Use the compensation method to solve these subtractions.

```
    5314              9612              7111
 – 2946           – 5032           – 3245
   2314
 +   54
```

....

....

Adding More than Two Numbers

Adding <u>more than two</u> numbers isn't too bad. Just make sure that you keep the
numbers <u>lined up</u> underneath each other — that way you don't get <u>confused</u>.

Try these:

```
                                        1645
                                        1245
    3614              2145               462
    2873              2289           + 2231
+    842           + 1111
```

....

Calculations — **Money and Real Life Problems**

Multi-Step Problems

All of the problems on this page have <u>more than one step</u>.
This means that the trick to working them out is to take each step <u>at a time</u>.

Professor Plank bought 2 balloons. One cost £3.40 and the other cost £4.78. How much change did he get from a £10 note?

....

....

One of the balloons is made of lead and is a load of rubbish.
Professor Plank gets £2.54 of his money back.

How much money does he have now?

....

Seb Bootio has been playing for 17 minutes of a football match that lasts an hour and a half. How long is it until half-time?

....

....

Simon has five 1p coins, three 2p coins, four 5p coins, three 10p coins and one 20p coin. Find as many different ways as you can to make 50p exactly from Simon's coins.

....

....

....

....

....

Money and Real Life Problems

Multi-Step Problems Using +, −, ×, ÷

You'll need to use <u>more</u> than just + and − with these questions.
Watch out for questions with <u>more than one step</u>.

Jake has to swim 30 miles to get to the underwater city of Atlantis.
He swam a sixth of the way with one oxygen tank, and two thirds
of the way with a different tank.

How far has Jake left to swim?

....

....

....

Tina Bopper collects music by her favourite band, The Meatballs.
She has 7 tapes with 20 songs each and 4 tapes with 25 songs each.

How many Meatball songs has she got altogether?

....

....

....

The four members of the Meatballs get paid £16
between them for playing a concert.

How many 50p packets of sauce can Tom
Meatball buy with his share of the concert money.

....

....

Rosemary eats a whole field of grass every 40 minutes.
Today she started eating at 10:20 am and ate 3 fields of grass.

What time did Rosemary finish eating?

....

....

....

Making Decisions

Deciding which Method to Use

It's no use being <u>brilliant</u> at maths if you don't
know when to use different <u>methods</u>.

Sometimes you don't need to spend <u>ages</u> writing out a sum in
columns because you could do it <u>in your head</u>. You need to be
able to <u>spot</u> when you've got to do the longer, boring methods.

EXAMPLE:

I'm sure you could do a sum like 43 + 6 in your head...

$$43 + 6 = \ldots\ldots\ldots$$ ⬅ Fill it in to prove that you can do it.

...but you might need to do 43 + 98 on paper:

$$\begin{array}{r} 43 \\ + \ 98 \\ \hline \ldots\ldots\ldots \end{array}$$

⬅ And try this one.

I would understand if you needed a calculator to work out 43 × 98:

$$43 \times 98 = \ldots\ldots\ldots\ldots$$ ⬅ You might as well do this one for good measure.

The best thing to do is to try working the question out <u>in your head first</u>.
If you <u>can't</u> do it, then think about whether you can do it <u>on paper</u>.
You should really only use your <u>calculator</u> if the question is
<u>too hard to do on paper</u>.

Decide how to do these questions, then solve them.
Use rough paper if you need to do any working out.

20 + 34 = ...	Method used: ....
20 × 34 = ...	Method used: ....
645 + 519 = ...	Method used: ....
94 − 35 = ...	Method used: ....
64 × 6 = ...	Method used: ....

Checking Results

Checking with Equivalent Calculations

We all make <u>mistakes</u> sometimes, even real <u>brainboxes</u> — so the best thing to do is to <u>check your answer</u> when you've finished a question.
You can check your answer by doing the question <u>back to front</u>.

Remember
+ is the opposite of −
and
× is the opposite of ÷

EXAMPLE: Check this sum: 456 + 345 = 801

Check it by doing the question back to front:

$$801 - 345 = 456 \checkmark$$

You could also check it by doing the other equivalent sum: $801 - 456 = 345 \checkmark$

Solve these additions and subtractions and check them with an equivalent statement.

281 + 375 = ... Check: .... − *375* = *281*

1246 − 614 = ... Check: .... + ... = ...

934 + 555 = ... Check: .... − .... = ...

EXAMPLE: Check 12 × 134 = 1608 with a calculator.

Check by either doing: $1608 \div 134 = 12 \checkmark$
or by doing: $1608 \div 12 = 134 \checkmark$

Doing the opposite is really easy when you know how.

Now have a go at these multiplications and divisions, and check them.

1320 ÷ 30 = ... Check: .... × .... = ...

20 × 46 = ... Check: .... ÷ .... = ...

1836 ÷ 51 = ... Check: .... × .... = ...

Maths fashion — striped sums and checked results...

It's a good idea to use a different sum when you check your answers. If you do the sum the same way both times you could make the same mistake both times.

Properties of Numbers

Understanding Number Sequences

Simple <u>number sequences</u> are just about <u>counting on</u> or <u>counting back</u>.

EXAMPLE:

Count on in 4s from zero to 20.

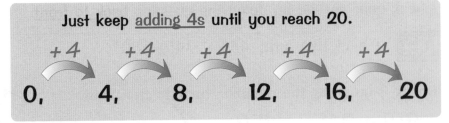

Just keep <u>adding 4s</u> until you reach 20.

+4   +4   +4   +4   +4

0,   4,   8,   12,   16,   20

Complete these number sequences.

2, 5, 8, ..., ..., ..., 20

6, 11, 16, ..., ..., ..., 36

40, 34, 28 ...., ..., ..., 4

Counting with <u>decimal numbers</u> is pretty easy as well. You still just <u>count up or down</u>, but be <u>careful</u> with the <u>decimal point</u>.

Fill in the next four terms in these sequences.

4.2, 6.2, 8.2, ..., ..., ..., ...

5.5, 5, 4.5, ..., ..., ..., ...

3.6, 4.2, 4.8, ..., ..., ..., ...

Counting with <u>negative numbers</u> isn't much harder — but remember to put the <u>minus</u> signs in.

Fill in the next four terms in these sequences.

–4, –8, –12, ..., ..., ..., ...

9, 6, 3, ..., ..., ..., ...

–27, –20, –13, ..., ..., ..., ...

Properties of Numbers

Factors of a Number

The <u>factors</u> of a number are any numbers that can be <u>multiplied together</u> to give the number.

EXAMPLES:

The number 10 has factors 1, 10, 2 and 5 because $1 \times 10 = 10$ and $2 \times 5 = 10$

The number 6 has factors 1, 6, 2, and 3 because $1 \times 6 = 6$ and $2 \times 3 = 6$

If a number has a factor, then it is <u>divisible</u> by that factor.
So 10 is <u>divisible</u> by 1, 10, 2 and 5.

If you think about it, <u>any</u> number in the 6 times table is divisible by 6,
so every number in the <u>6 times table</u> has a <u>factor of 6</u>.

Circle the numbers that have a factor of 6.

| 16 | 24 | 6 | 9 | 30 | 42 | 92 |

This time see if you can circle the factors of the number 64.

| 2 | | 64 | | | 1 | | 16 | | 12 |
| | 3 | | 5 | 15 | | 32 | | 4 | |

List all the factors of these numbers.

7 has factors .... and ....

14 has factors ...., ..., ... and ....

30 has factors ...., ..., ..., ..., ..., ..., ... and ....

Solving Problems

Reasoning About Numbers

More Number Puzzles

Don't be afraid to start by <u>guessing</u> with these puzzles, and keep guessing until you get the <u>right answer</u>.

Find three consecutive numbers which have a product of:

(Remember — "consecutive" means "next to each other".)

24: ....

210: ....

Find as many ways as you can of making 1000 by adding some of these numbers.

889   **268**

732   **431**

458   **111**

190

170   **640**

....

....

....

....

....

Find ways to complete this sum by putting in numbers instead of the shapes.

 $+$ $+$ $= 5$

....

....

....

Each tortoise stands for a missing number in this problem. Use your calculator to work out the missing numbers.

  $\times 5$ $= 2142$

....

....

....

....

Place Value

Multiplying and Dividing by 10 and 100

Multiplying by 10 or 100 is really easy — all you have to do is <u>move</u> everything to the <u>left</u> (and stick some 0s on the end if you need to). If you <u>multiply by 10</u>, move everything <u>1 space</u> to the left. If you <u>multiply by 100</u>, move <u>2 spaces</u>.

EXAMPLE: What is 72 × 100 ?

Move 72 two spaces to the left and put 0s in to fill up the gaps:

$$72 \times 100 = 7200$$

Dividing by 10 or 100 isn't too hard either — just <u>move</u> everything to the <u>right</u>.

EXAMPLE: What is 840 ÷ 10 ?

Move 840 one space to the right:

$$840 \div 10 = 84$$

Write in these missing numbers by working them out in your head.

Hello? I'd like to report some missing numbers.

23 × 10 =

64 × = 6400

600 ÷ 10 =

7600 ÷ 100 =

7400 ÷ = 740

47 × 100 =

 × 100 = 800

9000 ÷  = 900

100 fish for a tenner — that's plaice value...

There are some simple rules on this page that will save you a lot of time. If you multiply by 10 stick a '0' on and if you multiply by 100 stick a '00' on. If you divide by 10 move the numbers one space to the right and if you divide by 100 move them two places.

Numbers and the Number System	# Proportion

Estimating Simple Proportions

Estimating (or guessing) proportions is really useful. People estimate things all the time, like how far they need to walk to get to the shops.

EXAMPLE: Estimate the position of the arrow on the number line.

0   100

To help you find the approximate position of the arrow, you could mark quarters on the line.

0   100

That shows you that the arrow is between 25 and 50 on the line.

It is closer to 25, so you could say that the arrow is at about 35.

Estimate the positions of the worms on these number lines.

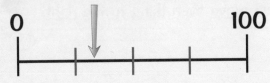

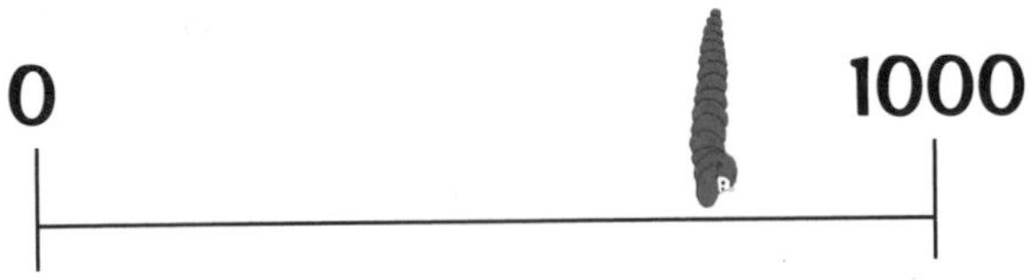

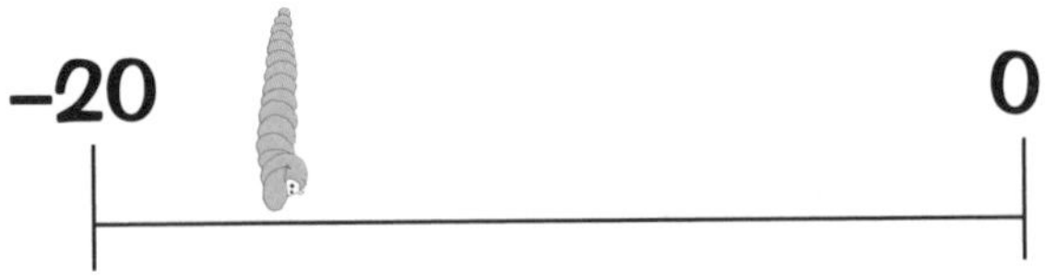

0   1000   −20   0

....

Estimating proportions of things that aren't on number lines isn't much harder — just work out about how much of something there is.

Estimate the amount of milk left in the bottle below. Write it as a fraction.

Draw a mark $\frac{1}{5}$ of the way up the tree trunk to help Vic cut the tree down.

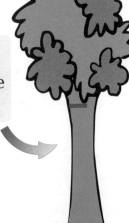

There is about .... of the milk left.

Temperature Difference

Calculating Temperature Rise and Fall

Reading temperatures from a <u>thermometer</u> is as easy as reading <u>any other scale</u>. The only <u>tricky</u> bit comes when you're working with <u>negative temperatures</u>, but I'm sure you can deal with that by now.

What temperature does this thermometer show?

Don't forget to put units in your answer.

....

°C –10   0   10   20   30   40

How about this one?

....

°C –10   0   10   20   30   40

The temperature outside Parky's house is 12 °C.
Parky only goes outside when the temperature falls to –5 °C.

By how many degrees must the temperature fall before he goes outside?

....

The temperature this morning was –9 °C, and has now risen by 21 °C. What is the temperature ?

....

The temperature in Colchester is 25 °C and in Kendal it is a bracing –8 °C.

What is the temperature difference between the towns?

....

Tim lives in Kendal and won't go outside until the temperature rises by 12 °C.

What temperature is that?

....

MATHS CLASSBOOK 5B

Using Calculators

Your friend the calculator, dropping back in to give a hand...

Draw arrows to show which buttons do these things.

To clear the whole calculation.

Finds the square root of the number entered.

| C | % | AC | √ | 6 | X | +/− | = | · |

To make a number negative.

The key you use at the end of a calculation.

To clear the last number you entered.

Use your calculator to answer these questions:

Charlie has made __3 kg__ of oozy gooey pond slime.
He's going to sell portions of __75__ g to the girls in his class.

How many portions can he sell?

....

If he sold all of them for 85p
each how much will he make?

....

His big brother gets really angry when he finds out Charlie used his new socks
to put the slime in and makes him pay back £10.

How much money did
Charlie make altogether?

....

Use a calculator to answer these questions. Do the bits in brackets first.

EXAMPLE: 2 + (3 × 6) = ...

If you typed in the
sum from left to right.

2 + 3 × 6 = *30*

BUT if you do
the <u>brackets first</u>   **3 × 6 =** *18*

then the
addition.   **2 + 18 =** *20*

The answer is quite different. This is the <u>right</u> way to do it.
ALWAYS WORK OUT THE BRACKETS FIRST

Now try these ones....

14 + (9 × 3) = ...   16 − (5 × 6) = ...   16 + (4 × 20) = ...

Understanding Division

Division always makes Whole Numbers Smaller

Handy Division Tips...

Division sums **WON'T** flip around to give the same answer.

$72 \div 9 = \underline{\quad 8 \quad}$

$9 \div 72 = \underline{\quad 0.125 \quad}$

You **CAN'T** divide a number by **ZERO**.

See how quickly you can answer these division questions:

There are lots of different ways a sum can tell you that you need to divide.

These are just words — once you've worked out you need to use ÷, then it's all straightforward.

Divide 56 by 7 ....

How many groups of 6 in 48? ....

What are the factors of 36? ....

Share 8 between 48 ....

Is 156 divisible by 6? ....

Ludwick Lop-a-Lot <u>cuts off</u> anything he can get his axe to. He's spied Mrs Clapham's wonderful **3m** mailbox post.

How many bits will he make if he chops it into 12 cm bits?

....

÷ Sums can be Written in Different Ways

All these sums tell you to divide 24 by 3: $\frac{1}{3}$ of 24  24 ÷ 3  $\frac{24}{3}$

Fill in these blanks

$\frac{63}{7} = \quad ....$

$\frac{54}{.....} = 18$

$......... \div 9 = 8$

$172 \div 4 = \quad ....$

$......... \div 21 = 90$

$\frac{1}{3}$ of 9 = ...

They're coming out of the page at me — 3D vision...

Recognising a division sum when you see one is the first hurdle — the sums above are all division sums written in different ways. All you have to do then is answer them.

Calculations

Understanding Division

Quotient is a funny word.

When you divide one number by another the answer you get is called the quotient.

$$56 \div 8 = \underline{\;\;7\;\;}$$ **QUOTIENT**

When the quotient isn't a whole number we can write it as a...

Fraction

$$43 \div 9 = \underline{4\frac{7}{9}}$$

Decimal   or we can **Round** it.

$$43 \div 9 = \underline{4.77} \longrightarrow \underline{\;\;5\;\;}$$

Do these divisions and write the answers as fractions.

EXAMPLE: $38 \div 8$

We're dividing by 8 so let's think in 8's

1. Find the <u>nearest whole multiple</u> of 8 that will go into 38. $= \;\; 4 \times 8 = 32$

2. What is "<u>left over</u>" from this whole number (the remainder). $= \;\; 38 - 32 = 6$

3. Write this as a <u>fraction of 8</u> and then simplify it if you can. $= \;\; 4\frac{6}{8} \;\; = \;\; 4\frac{3}{4}$

$66 \div 8 = \;\;...............$ $35 \div 6 = \;\;...............$ $57 \div 9 = \;\;...............$ $41 \div 7 = \;\;...............$

....

Do these divisions and write the answers as decimals.

A decimal, a fraction, a decimal, a fraction....

EXAMPLE: $61 \div 4$

$15 \times 4 = 60$

$61 - 60 = 1$

$61 \div 4 = 15\frac{1}{4} = 15.25$

Find the <u>nearest whole multiple</u> of 4 and the <u>remainder</u>.

then <u>convert</u> the fraction part to a decimal.

$$1 \div 4 = \underline{\;\;0.25\;\;}$$

$91 \div 10 = \;\;...............$ $46 \div 5 = \;\;...............$ $29 \div 2 = \;\;...............$ $34 \div 4 = \;\;...............$

....

Mental Strategies for × and ÷

× 2 To Double and ÷ 2 Halve

Try these sums using halving and doubling sums:

Half 256 busy ants: $256 = 200 + 50 + 6 \rightarrow 100 + 25 + 3 = 128$

split the number into simple <u>H</u>, <u>T</u> and <u>U</u> then double or halve these separately.

Double 53 chillies = ...

Half 98 golf balls = ...

Half 356 smelly socks = ...

Double 78 ice cubes = ...

In a multiplication sum you can double or halve one of the numbers as long as you do the <u>OPPOSITE</u> to another number.

Use these tricks to answer these questions.

$16 \times 5 = \underline{\quad 8 \times 10 \quad} = \underline{\quad 80 \quad}$

<u>DOUBLE</u> numbers ending in 5 and <u>HALVE</u> the other number.

$13 \times 14 = \underline{\quad 13 \times 7 \times 2 \quad} = \underline{\quad 91 \times 2 = 182 \quad}$

halve the <u>EVEN</u> number then double the product.

$35 \times 14 = $ ....

$16 \times 51 = $ ....

$45 \times 6 = $ ....

$12 \times 23 = $ ....

Travis needs help to double up his baking orders. Use your skills to fill in the list for him.

Travis's Quick List

$1 \times 25 = 25$

$2 \times 25 = $ ....

$....... \times 25 = 100$

$8 \times 25 = $ ....

$16 \times 25 = $ ....

Mental Strategies for × and ÷

You can double and halve <u>fractions</u> too...

Here's the trick.

What's a $\frac{1}{6}$ of 300?

A sixth is hard to work out.

It's easier to <u>double</u> the fraction to a $\frac{1}{3}$.

Multiply this by 300. $\frac{1}{3} \times 300 = \underline{100}$

Then <u>halve</u> the answer, to get a sixth of 300. $100 \div 2 = \underline{50}$

Double a Fraction — the Bottom gets Smaller

$\frac{1}{8}$ of 200 = ...

$\frac{1}{4}$ of 300 = ...

$\frac{1}{6}$ of 120 = ...

$\frac{1}{20}$ of 900 = ...

$\frac{1}{4}$ of 500 = ...

$\frac{1}{5}$ of 250 = ...

 All this halving and doubling is putting me in a spin...

 <u>HALVE</u> this one to $\frac{1}{10}$ and then <u>DOUBLE</u> to get the right answer.

Use Factors of Big Numbers to × and ÷ Easily

2 and 3 are <u>FACTORS</u> of 6 because 2 × 3 = 6.

$15 \times 6 = \underline{15 \times 3 \times 2}$

1. $\underline{15 \times 3} = \underline{45}$ × by one factor
15 × 3 is easy to do.
2. $\underline{45 \times 2} = \underline{90}$ × the answer by the other factor.

Use factors to answer these.

$15 \times 6 = \underline{90}$

$13 \times 8 =$ ....

$21 \times 14 =$ ....

$7 \times 15 =$ ....

$90 \div 6 = \underline{90 \div 3 = 30, \ 30 \div 2 =}$

$200 \div 8 =$ ....

$84 \div 14 =$ ....

Multiplication Methods

Grids help you split up numbers into H, T and U

EXAMPLE: 356 × 9

Break up the number into <u>H</u>, <u>T</u> and <u>U</u>

356 = 300 ←——Hundreds

  50 ←——Tens

   6 ←——Units

Use the <u>grid</u> to multiply each of these numbers separately by 9. Then <u>add</u> all the products at the end.

×	300	50	6
9	2700	450	54

= 2700 + 450 + 54 ....

= 3204 ....

Use the grid method to do these multiplications.

493 × 6 =

×			

= ....

251 × 7 =

×			

= ....

834 × 4 =

×			

= ....

Use the same method with these slightly bigger numbers:

72 × 38 =

×	70	2
30	2100	60
8		

= 2100 + 60 ....

= .... + ...

= 2160 + ... = ...

54 × 98 =

×		

= .... + ...

= .... + ...

= .... + ... = ...

Long Multiplication

There are different ways to multiply. I'm afraid you've got to <u>know</u> how to do them all, <u>BUT</u> the tip is to choose the one <u>you like best</u> and use that.

24 × 43 = ...

```
              24
           ×  43
24 × 40      960
24 × 3        72  +
            1032
```

36 × 27 = ...

```
              36
           ×  27
36 × 20
36 × 7          +
```

342 × 9 = ...

```
             342
           ×   9
300 × 9
40 × 9
2 × 9          +
```

Solving Problems	# Money and Real Life Problems

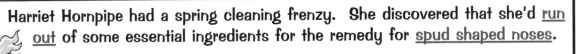

Decimal Sums with Pounds & Pence

Harriet Hornpipe had a spring cleaning frenzy. She discovered that she'd <u>run out</u> of some essential ingredients for the remedy for <u>spud shaped noses</u>.

She buys <u>£9.63</u> worth of lizard cream, <u>£4.16</u> of rotten eggs and <u>£15.27</u> of the essential ingredient — bat juice.

> How much did she spend altogether?

....

Harriet's enormous pet snail, Willy, drank all her expensive <u>broom lubricating oil</u>. The local garage sells it for <u>64.2p</u> per litre.

> How much will it cost her to fill up her five litre can?

....

Harriet has been saving up to visit her sister. She's saved <u>85p a week</u> for <u>1 year</u>.

> How much has she saved?

....

Harriet posts her sister a rocket-propelled pig to let her know that she's on her way. She's <u>not sure</u> of the price but she has <u>two 25p</u> and <u>two 35p</u> Propeller Pig Stamps.

> What different amounts could she pay for with these stamps?

....

....

Harriet is going on a shopping trip to several different countries. The Cheesy Exchange man gives these exchange rates for <u>£1</u>.

> How many pesetas, francs and dollars will she get for £5?

£1 = 220 pesetas so £5 = 220 x 5 = 1100 pesetas

....

....

....

EXCHANGE RATE
220 Spanish Pesetas
8.7 French Francs
1.6 Sorcerer's Dollars

Number Stories & Decisions

Think about what the Sum is Asking You to Do

When you're looking at a puzzle, question, story or sum you have to first <u>DECIDE</u> what they're asking you to do.

There could be a lot of rubbish or <u>extra information</u> that isn't needed at all for you to answer the question. Don't worry about those bits, just leave them.

Once you've decided what the question is asking, then decide what you're going to <u>DO</u>. Decide whether you will +, −, ÷ or ×, find <u>fractions,</u> or even do <u>2 things</u>.

It's <u>all your choice</u>, so just pop the right sign in and go for it.

Make up your own number stories for these sums.

$572 - 25 = 547$

572 electronic zapping robots were made in one day.

25 of them were missing the zapitron, so only 547 were working.

$1435 + 3245 = 4680$

....

....

$38.7 \times 24 = 928.8$

Use any silly idea or combination of things to make up your stories.

....

....

$564 \div 8 = 70.5$

....

Fill in the right signs in these sums.

$319 \bigpentagon 274 = 593$ $\qquad$ $572 \bigpentagon 291 = 281$ $\qquad$ $19 \bigpentagon 52 = 988$

$18 \bigpentagon 6 = 108$ $\qquad$ $572 \bigpentagon 291 = 863$ $\qquad$ $228 \bigpentagon 38 = 6$

Calculations

Approximating Sums

Rounding Numbers to Estimate Answers

If you need to make a quick guess, a good way is to approximate by rounding.

EXAMPLE: What is 413 + 124?

To do a quick approximation we can round each number to the nearest 100:

$$400 + 100 = 500$$

So by our approximation, the answer should be just over 500.

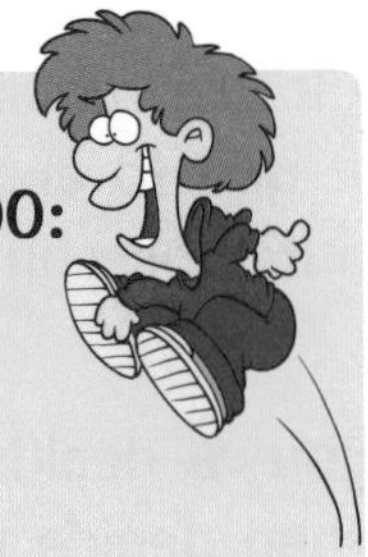

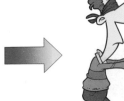

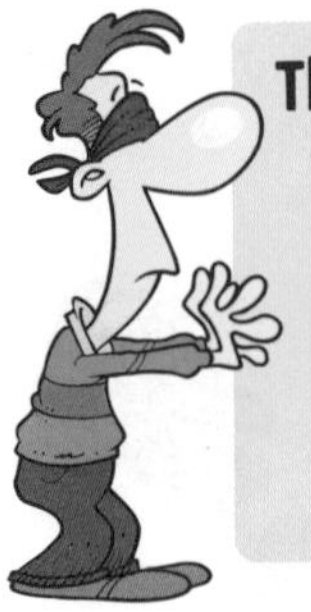

Then do the sum:

$$\begin{array}{r} 413 \\ +\ 124 \\ \hline 537 \end{array}$$

EXAMPLE: What is 32 × 19?

Multiplications look even harder than addition and subtraction. To stop me getting it all wrong, I can make a quick check by rounding to the nearest 10:

$$30 \times 20 = 600$$

The answer should be about 600.
Try it on a calculator to see if that's right.

$$32 \times 19 = 608$$

So the estimate was pretty accurate this time.

Estimate these by rounding first then work them out.

Use a calculator if you really need to.

421 + 109: Estimate: .... + ... = ... Answer: ....

21 × 9: Estimate: .... × .... = ... Answer: ....

585 – 214: Estimate: .... – .... = ... Answer: ....

490 ÷ 98: Estimate: .... ÷ .... = ... Answer: ....

818 – 386: Estimate: .... – .... = ... Answer: ....

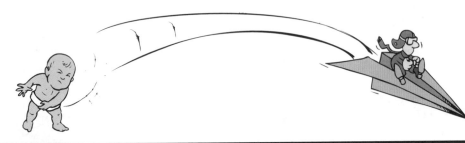

Fractions

Fractions and Division

We've already figured out that <u>fractions</u> are just a neat way of showing a <u>division</u>.

Remember, $\frac{1}{2}$ means "1 divided by 2".

EXAMPLE: Work out $\frac{1}{3}$ of 15.

If there is a 1 on the <u>top</u> of the fraction <u>(the numerator)</u>, then all you have to do is divide by the <u>bottom</u> number <u>(the denominator)</u>.

$$15 \times \frac{1}{3} = \frac{15}{3} = 5$$

EXAMPLE: Work out $\frac{3}{5}$ of 10.

This bit's really important — make sure you understand it.

If the numerator <u>isn't</u> a 1 then it's a <u>bit</u> harder. Here's the trick:

$$10 \times \frac{3}{5} = \frac{10 \times 3}{5} = \frac{30}{5} = 6$$

Multiply by the numerator first...   ...and THEN divide by the denominator.

Use this method to work out these.

$12 \times \frac{2}{3} = \dfrac{24}{3} = 8$

$20 \times \frac{4}{10} = \dots = \dots$

$20 \times \frac{3}{4} = \dots = \dots$

$50 \times \frac{2}{10} = \dots = \dots$

Dave can lift an <u>18 kg</u> weight but Paul can only lift $\frac{2}{3}$ as much.

What is the difference between the weights Dave and Paul can lift?

(work step by step)

....

....

Numbers and the
Number System

Decimals

Calculations with Mixed Units

Questions with <u>mixed units</u> need a bit of <u>sorting out</u> before you can do them.
The first thing to do is to change them so that everything is in the same unit.

EXAMPLE: What is 3 km + 200 m?

There are <u>2 ways</u> of doing this — you could
convert everything into <u>kilometres</u> or <u>metres</u>.
It's usually <u>easier</u> to change into the <u>smallest</u>
<u>unit</u> in the question.

Change everything into <u>metres</u>:

3000 m + 200 m = 3200 m

If you want, you could turn the
answer back into <u>kilometres</u>, so the
answer is **3.2** km.

Use the same method to solve these mixed unit questions.

2 kg + 300 g = ...*2000 g*.... + ...*300 g*.... = ...*2300 g*....

5 m + 60 cm = ... + ... = ...

10 m + 4 km = ... + ... = ...

3 kg – 1500 g = ... – .... = ...

15 cm – 20 mm = ... – .... = ...

4 km – 15 m = ... – .... = ...

A Useful Reminder

10 mm = 1 cm	100 cm = 1 m
1000 m = 1 km	1000 g = 1 kg

Percentages

Numbers and the Number System

The Percentage (%) Sign

A percentage is like a fraction, but all percentages are the number of parts in every hundred, like this:

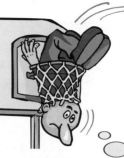

$$\frac{30}{100}$$ We write this as: 30%

Think of percentages as a special type of fraction. Take a look at these:

100% = one whole
50% = one half
25% = one quarter
10% = one tenth

If you look around you'll see % signs everywhere, like on clothes labels or cereal packets.

EXAMPLE:

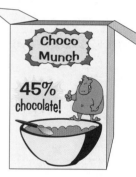

45% chocolate means that if you could divide the ingredients up into 100 equal parts, 45 of them would be chocolate.

We know that 50% is the same as a half. That means that just less than half of the Choco Munch is chocolate.

Write these fractions as percentages.

$\frac{15}{100}$ salt = ... %

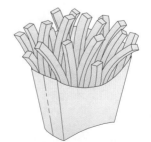

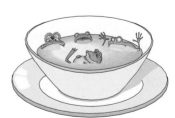

$\frac{87}{100}$ custard = ... %

$\frac{45}{100}$ fizz = ... %

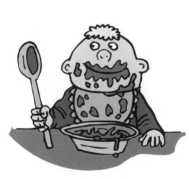

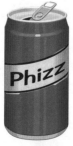

Cats have Percentages — dogs have Woofcentages...

Percentages are always parts of 100 — this means that 100% is the whole thing. Writing out a percentage as a fraction is easy — if it's 47% write 47 above 100 in the fraction.

Percentages

Finding Percentages

Finding percentages of numbers is <u>really easy</u> if the numbers are <u>multiples of 100</u>.
All you have to do is <u>multiply</u>.

EXAMPLE: What is 35% of 200 ?

Start with something that is <u>easy to work out</u>.
You can say that:

35% of 100 = 35   because <u>35% means 35 out of 100</u>.

Now all you have to do to find <u>35% of 200</u> is to <u>multiply by 2</u>.

35% of 200 = 35 × 2 = 70

Work out these percentages using the method above.

25% of 300 = ...*25*............ × ....*3*............ = ...*75*............

50% of 200 = ... × .... = ...

30% of 500 = ... × .... = ...

15% of 300 = ... × .... = ...

75% of 200 = ... × .... = ...

20% of 50 = ... × .... = ...

The last question's tricky.
See if you can think of a fraction
that might help you work it out.

Percentages

Changing Fractions to Percentages

Percentages are just a <u>special type of fraction</u> that always has <u>100 on the bottom</u>.
That means some percentages are the same as <u>pretty simple</u> fractions.

EXAMPLE:

Cancelled down

$$10\% = \frac{10}{100} = \frac{1}{10} = 0.1$$

10 out of 100

You should remember decimals
like this from earlier on.

Here's some of the other <u>really useful</u> percentages:

$1\% = 0.01 = \frac{1}{100}$ $50\% = 0.5 = \frac{1}{2}$

$20\% = 0.2 = \frac{1}{5}$ $75\% = 0.75 = \frac{3}{4}$

$25\% = 0.25 = \frac{1}{4}$ $100\% = 1$

Work out the shaded fraction and percentage of each shape.

Write the fraction here.   And put the percentage here.

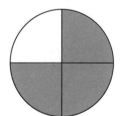

Shaded area = ... = ...

Shaded area = ... = ...

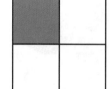

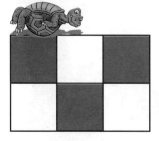

Shaded area = ... = ...

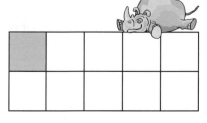

Shaded area = ... = ...

Numbers and the Number System

Percentages

Finding Percentages by using Fractions

I know percentages can be a <u>real pain</u> — but sometimes they're <u>really easy</u> to work out if you know this little trick.

You've already seen that some <u>percentages</u> mean the <u>same thing</u> as a <u>fraction</u>.

EXAMPLE: If you need to know 75% of 44, remember 75% is the same as $\frac{3}{4}$.

First work out $\frac{1}{4}$ (25%) of 44. $\Longrightarrow$ $\frac{1}{4}$ of 44 = 11

Once you know that, you can work out $\frac{3}{4}$ by multiplying 11 by 3.

$$\frac{3}{4} \text{ of } 44 = 33$$

Fill in the missing fractions and percentages, just to show you've been awake.

50% = ...

$\frac{3}{4}$ = ...

$\frac{1}{4}$ = ...

10% = ...

Try these for size, using the new method:

50% of 38: ....

25% of 88: ....

10% of 140: ....

75% of 64: ....

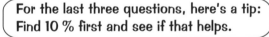

For the last three questions, here's a tip: Find 10 % first and see if that helps.

60% of 40: ....

30% of 60: ....

90% of 50: ....

Ratio and Proportion

"For Every" Questions are about Proportions

Proportion is pretty easy — it's all about multiplying and dividing.

EXAMPLE:

Matt and Nic share everything, but Matt makes sure he always gets a bigger share. He gets 2 slices of pizza for every 1 that Nic gets.

This means that:
Matt has twice as many slices of pizza as Nic.
Nic has half as many slices as Matt.

Matt has $\frac{2}{3}$ of the total number of slices and Nic has $\frac{1}{3}$ of the total number.

If Nic has 4 slices of pizza, Matt has twice as many, so he has 8 slices.
If Matt has 18 slices of pizza, Nic has half that amount, so she has 9 slices.

A recipe needs 3 daffodils for every 2 eggs.

Garry puts 6 eggs in. How many daffodils does he need?   ....

Matt and Nic use the same recipe. They put 18 daffodils into the pot. How many eggs do they need?   ....

How many things in total are in Matt and Nic's pot?   ....

Garry and Tim are playing some groovy tunes on the jukebox.
For every 5 songs Garry plays he lets Tim choose 2 more.

Tim chooses 4 songs. How many tunes does Garry choose?   ....

Garry picks 35 songs. How many choices does Tim have this time?   ....

Yesterday Tim picked 6 songs. How many songs did the two of them play that day?

....

....

48

Organising and Interpreting Data

Predictions about things can be Checked

At the Dodgy Brothers' Travelling Funfair, 8 kids from Year 5 have entered in the Frog Flipping Championship and the Shabby Shot Game.

I predict that the most common scores will be 9 out of 10 frogs flipped and 8 shots out of 10 in.

How would we go about checking this prediction?

Let's start by writing the scores down so it's clearer. A table makes this much easier. It even has a special name — it's called a DATABASE.

SCORES FOR FROG FLIPPING

Allie 9, Steven 9, Chuck 9, Bertie 8, Polly 9, Frannie 7.

SCORES FOR SHABBY SHOTS

Allie 6, Steven 2, Chuck 8, Bertie 9, Polly 6, Frannie 6.

The most common score is also called the MODE.

Fill in the table with all the scores and answer the questions.

Name	Frog Flipping Score (out of 10)	Shabby Shot Score (out of 10)
Allie	9	6
Steven		
Chuck		
Bertie		
Polly		
Frannie		

What's the most common score in each game?

Frog Flipping ....

Shabby Shot ....

Put the scores in order to find the maximum and minimum scores of both?

Frog Flipping ....

Shabby Shot ....

Find the difference between the highest and the lowest scores? This is the RANGE.

Frog Flipping .... Shabby Shot ....

I predicted that the MOST COMMON SCORE would be 9 out of 10 for frog flipping. The MODE, or most common score, was 9 — so that prediction was RIGHT. For the shabby shots, the mode was 6 and not 8 as in the prediction, so it was WRONG.

The RANGE showed us the SPREAD of scores from highest to lowest. The first one was only 2, so most scores were very close together (at most only 2 points different). But in shabby shots, the biggest gap was 7 — so we could say the scores were very spread out.

Probability

Bar Charts are used for Whole Number Data

<u>Frequency</u> is just a big word for how often something happens.

We often talk about the <u>frequency of an event</u>. The event could be anything from scoring goals, rolling a six on a dice or getting hit on the head.

The frequency tells you the number of times something happened, like how many goals were scored, the number of sixes rolled, or how often you were hit.

Bar charts are a good way of <u>showing frequencies</u> they're much easier to read.

Look at the bar chart showing the frequency of goals scored by Barrow FC in last season's matches.

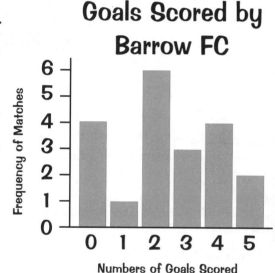

Goals Scored by Barrow FC

How many matches did Barrow play in?

Total matches = 4 + 1 +

....

....

There were <u>4 matches</u> in the first column.
There was <u>1 match</u> in the second column ...

What was the maximum number of goals Barrow scored in a match?

....

In how many of their matches did Barrow score <u>MORE</u> than 3 goals?

....

What was the <u>MODE</u> — the most common number of goals?

....

How likely are Barrow to score 7 goals in a match next season if they play in the same league as this year?

....

Sheepergrass — top of the bar charts...

Take your time to work out what each question is asking — Remember to read all the labels on a bar chart and remember that frequency means how often something happens.

Plotting Line Graphs

Line Graphs are all wiggly and pointy because the line joins up the measurement points <u>across</u> the graph.

It's just like playing join the dots.

Draw your own line graph from these results.

Bill's inflatable cow Clementine has a <u>hole</u> in it, so he keeps having to <u>pump it up</u>. He measures its height every hour from <u>10 am</u> to <u>3 pm</u>, and writes down the results.

10:00 am — 90 cm
11:00 am — 62 cm
12:00 pm — 15 cm
1:00 pm — 44 cm
2:00 pm — 100 cm
3:00 pm — 2 cm

Plot the point by reading up from the time and then across from the height. Mark a cross where the 2 lines meet. Then join up all the points.

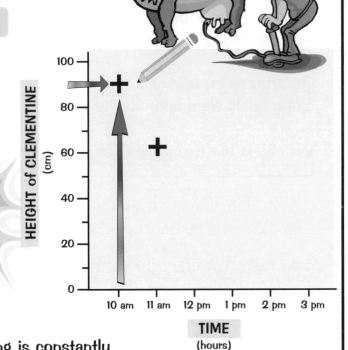

Line Graphs are used when what we are measuring is constantly changing between each point — like heights, temperatures or volumes.

Practise again with plotting the points and drawing a line graph, from this question.

Professor Nincompoop is doing an experiment on bean-eating slugs. He recorded the weight of his biggest slug Sue over a week.

Sue weighed...

240 g on Mon
300 g on Tues
390 g on Wed
270 g on Thurs
285 g on Fri
325 g on Sat
440 g on Sun

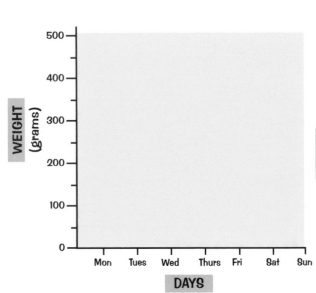

Between which days did Sue lay eggs?

....

Using a Calculator

Round .999999 up to the Closest Whole Number

0.99999 is a <u>recurring</u> number that might come up on your calculator screen.
This is so close to the next whole number it's silly if we don't <u>round it up</u>.

What would you round these numbers up to?

7.9999999 ➡ ....

144.9999999 ➡ ....   23.9999999 ➡ ....

58.9999999 ➡ ....   99.9999999 ➡ ....

Write down the two closest whole numbers that these decimals fall between.

18.75 is between ....*18*.... and ....*19*.....

↖ 18.75 is just 18 + 0.75. So we know the first WHOLE number it's
bigger than is 18, so the closest one it's smaller than must be 19.

91.55 is between .... and ....

16.493 is between .... and ....

212.74 is between .... and ....

0.25 is between .... and ....

Carly makes flamingo hair clips. She uses **233.33** feathers to make 100 clips.

How many feathers does she use for one clip?   What two numbers is this between?

.... ÷ .... = ... ➡ is between .... and ....

How many feathers does she use for three clips?
Round your answer to the nearest whole number.   ....

| Measures, Shape and Space | **Reflection** |

Test for Reflective Symmetry in all Polygons

Does a square have reflective symmetry?

Polygons are just flat shapes with 3 or more sides and the same number of angles. Some of these shapes have <u>REFLECTIVE SYMMETRY</u>.

A shape has reflective symmetry if it has an <u>AXIS of SYMMETRY</u>. An <u>AXIS of SYMMETRY</u> is exactly the same as a <u>line of symmetry</u>.

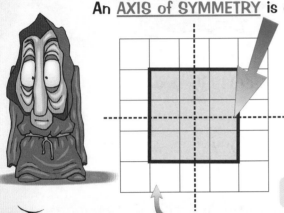

We can find this by using a <u>mirror</u>, or even by <u>cutting</u> out and <u>folding</u> the shape.

The shape is <u>the same</u> on both sides of an axis of symmetry.

We have found 2 axes of symmetry So the square has <u>reflective symmetry</u>.

Draw two more lines of symmetry on the square.

It helps to draw the shape on squared paper.

Finish drawing these shapes and work out whether they have reflective symmetry.

Trapezium

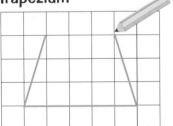

Number of lines of symmetry:

....

Hexagon

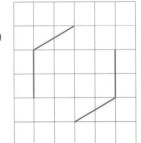

Number of lines of symmetry:

....

Scalene Triangle

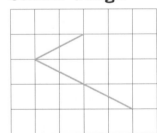

Number of lines of symmetry:

....

Draw a reflection of William's footprint across the mirror line.

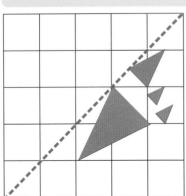

Did you know that a REGULAR POLYGON has the same number of sides as lines of symmetry...

Translation

Translation — just Moving Shapes Around

Translate these shapes 4 units to the right and draw them in the new position.

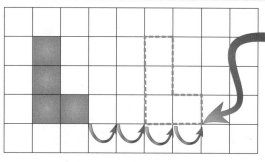

Pick a point on the corner of the shape, and move that 4 points along, then trace in the rest of the shape.

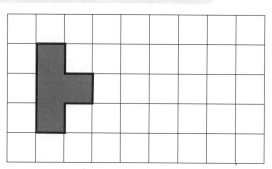

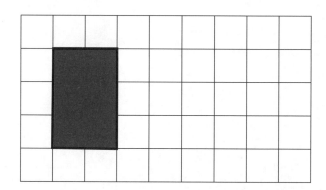

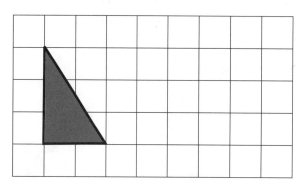

Translation and Reflection

It's time to use translation and reflection together to create a beautiful pattern.

1 Carry out these translations.
1) Purple cross, 7 units to the right.
2) Green shape, 3 units to the left.
3) Blue square, 9 units to the right.

2 Now reflect all the shapes in the mirror line.

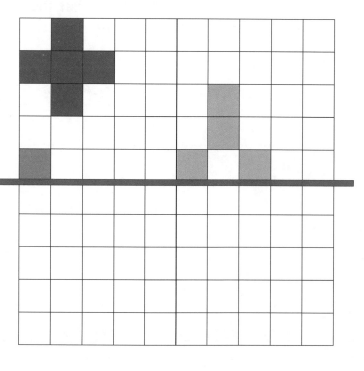

Directions and Grid Positions

Taissa has a cheeky rat in her kitchen eating all her food. She decides to go and buy a <u>remote controlled rat catcher</u>.

Taissa makes the robot move by typing in <u>grid co-ordinates</u>. She has to put in the co-ordinates to avoid Milly the Cleaning Elephant, her lazy little brother and other kitchen furniture.

She starts it at <u>co-ordinate (0, 1)</u>
and puts in the points (4, 1), (4, 3), (5, 3), (5, 6).

Mark these points on the map of the kitchen and draw in the route.

(0, 1) — Remember the first number is for <u>**ACROSS**</u> and the
second number is for <u>UP</u>.

She has to write down the directions that the robot goes if it starts at (0, 1) and follows the points that she put in.

Finish off the directions for her:

Go forward 4 units before you hit Milly. Turn left and go forward...
....

....

....

Draw a different route for the robot to get back to (0, 1).

Write down the points where the robot has to turn.

....

Aaaaargh, too many squares — G'rid of 'em...

Co-ordinates are a way of letting you know where you are. Remember that a point has to be given by reading **ACROSS FIRST** and then by **READING UP**.

Directions and Grid Positions

Grids can be divided up into 4 quadrants

A GRID is like a BIG square. It's easier to plot points on it when it's split up with axes.

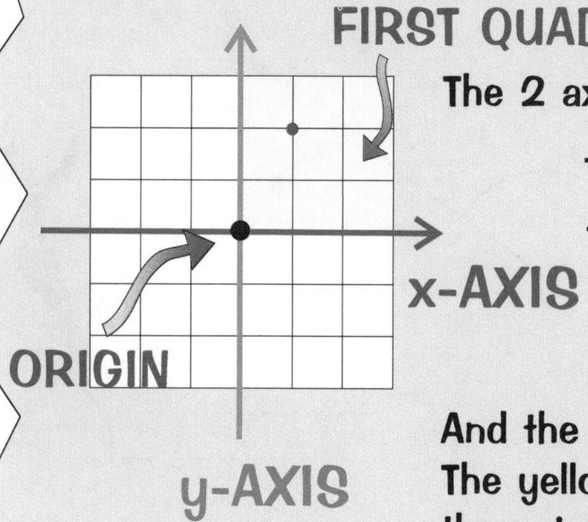

FIRST QUADRANT

The 2 axes have special names.....

— the red one is the x-AXIS and always goes ACROSS.

— the blue one is the y-AXIS and always goes UP.

x-AXIS

The point where they cross is called the ORIGIN and it's written as (0, 0).

ORIGIN

And the 4 bits the grid is divided into are called QUADRANTS. The yellow one is the FIRST QUADRANT because all the points in there are positive.

y-AXIS

What are the co-ordinates of the point marked on the grid?

ACROSS is along the x-axis and **UP** is along the y-axis.

Start at the origin (0, 0).

Read across 1 line and then up 2. So the point is (1, 2)

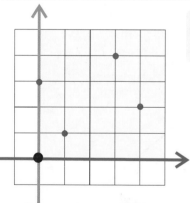

Write down the co-ordinates of the 4 points on this grid.

What shape do the points make?

We call it cattle gridlock!

Join all the points together on the grid.

Plot the points (1, 1), (3, 1), (3, 4), (2, 5) and (1, 4).

What shape do they make?

INGRID BURGER

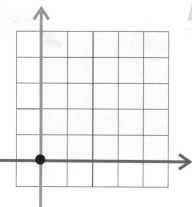

Measures, Shape and Space	*Calculating Angles*

Compare Angles *with Ones You Know*

You know what <u>right angles</u> and <u>straight lines</u> look like — so when you've got to estimate an angle, work out roughly how much <u>bigger</u> or <u>smaller</u> it is than one of those.

Estimate the size of these angles, to the nearest 5°.

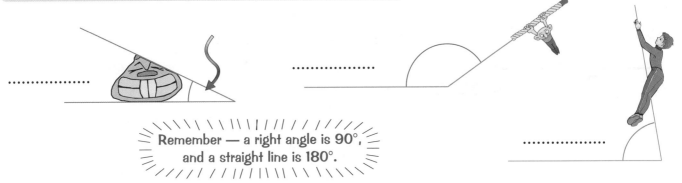

....

....

....

Remember — a right angle is 90°, and a straight line is 180°.

Measure *Angles with a* <u>Protractor</u>

To get the exact answer, you need to use a protractor.

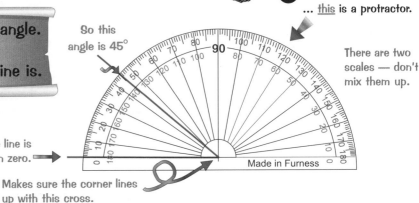

1) Put the protractor on top of the angle.
2) Line up the zero with one line.
3) Read the scale where the other line is.

So this angle is 45°

No, that's a <u>tractor</u>...

... <u>this</u> is a protractor.

There are two scales — don't mix them up.

Make sure the line is exactly on zero.

Makes sure the corner lines up with this cross.

Made in Furness

Now measure these angles:

....

....

....

....

Calculating Angles

Measures, Shape and Space

Draw Angles with a Protractor

EXAMPLE: Draw an angle of 40°.

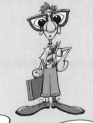

Drawing angles is dead easy. Start off with a line, and mark a dot on it.

Put the protractor so the cross is exactly <u>on</u> the dot and the line goes through <u>zero</u>.

Read where the angle is on the protractor and then mark another dot at its edge.

40°
Made in Furness

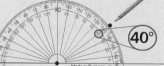

Draw a straight line through both dots and you've drawn your angle.

Use a protractor to draw these angles:

25°
40°
135°
115°

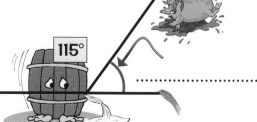

Calculate Angles in a Straight Line

I only allow cucumber trained cowboys in the Great Cucumber Shoot Out.

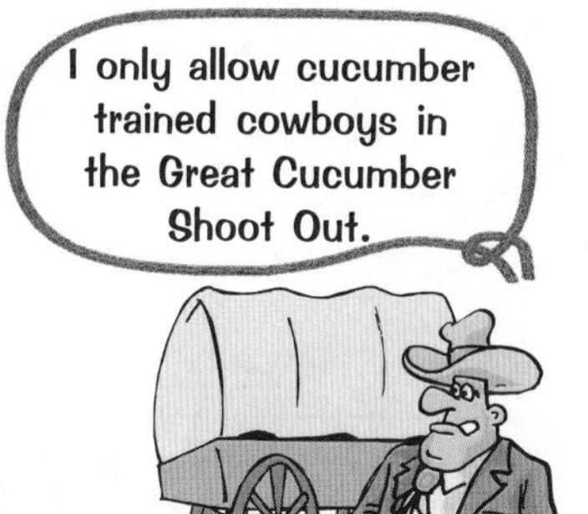

Remember all straight lines are 180°. So if you're given one angle, just subtract this from 180° to get the other one.

What sizes are these angles?

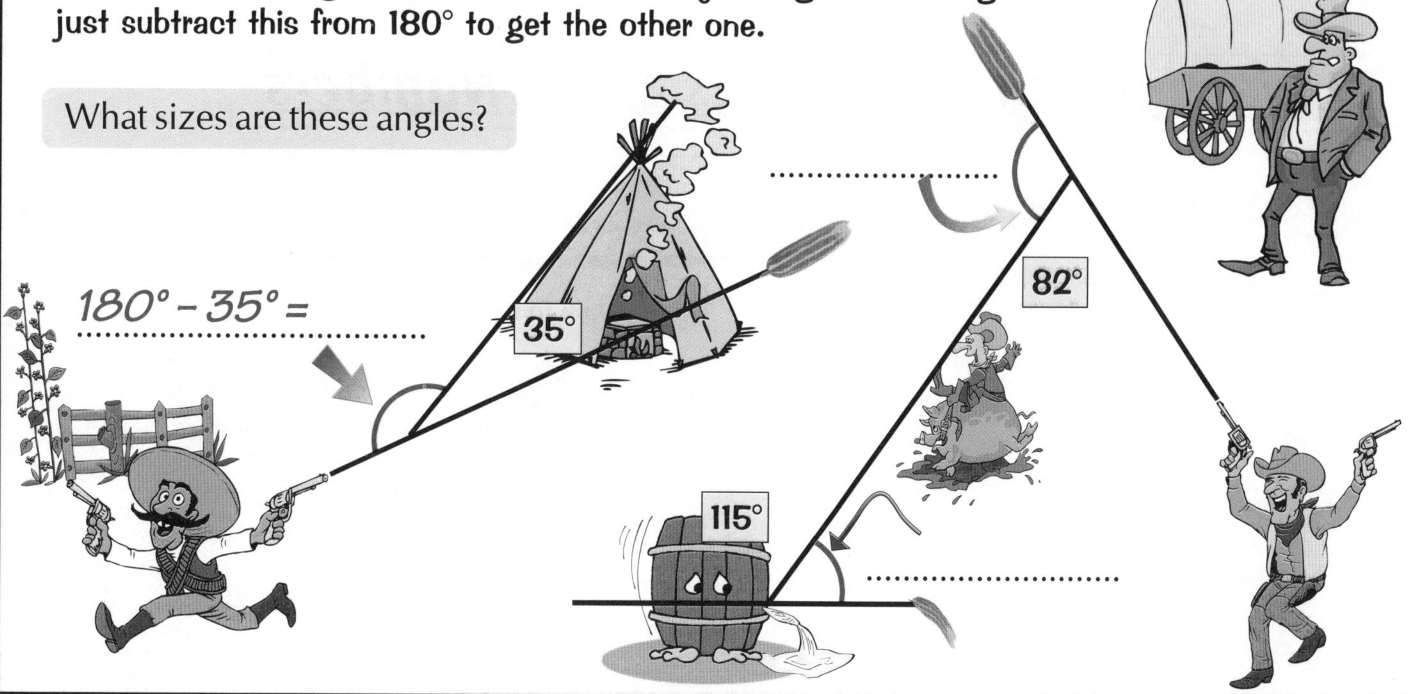

180° − 35° = ...
35°
82°
....
115°
....

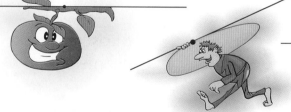

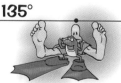

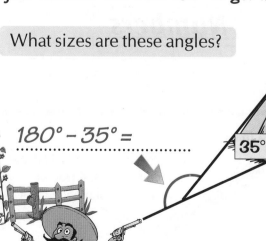

Investigating Numbers & Shapes

When you're asked to <u>investigate</u> things in maths you <u>don't</u> need a silly hat and a magnifying glass — you just need to find out whether or not something is true.

Investigating Statements about <u>Shapes</u>

The best way to see if a rule <u>works</u> is to test it on a few <u>examples</u>. If you find an example that shows that the rule doesn't work, double check it to make sure.

Use examples to investigate this rule.

To work out the perimeter of a regular polygon you multiply the length of one side by the number of sides.

Measure the perimeter and then work it out using the rule:

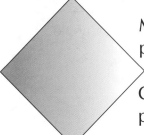

Measured
perimeter = ...

Calculated
perimeter = ...

Measured
perimeter = ...

Calculated
perimeter = ...

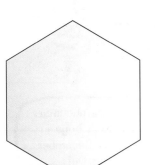

Measured
perimeter = ...

Calculated
perimeter = ...

Measured
perimeter = ...

Calculated
perimeter = ...

Is the rule true? ....

Investigating Statements about <u>Numbers</u>

Use examples to investigate this rule.

If you multiply 9 by any single-digit number (except '0'), the digits in the answer always add up to nine.

$9 \times 6 = 54 \implies 5 + 4 = \textcircled{9}$
....

This one follows the rule.

Try four other examples to test the rule and then circle true or false in the sentence below.

....

....

....

....

After the investigation I think that the rule is
TRUE / FALSE

Converting Units

Converting Decimals and Fractions of Units

Convert these into the smaller units written after the dots.

1.3 m = __130__ cm

5.1 kg = ... g

7.2 l = ... ml

100 centimetres in a metre so :

× 100

CONVERT TO

m → cm

1000 grams in a kilogram so :

× 1000

CONVERT TO

g → kg

1000 millilitres in a litre so :

× 1000

CONVERT TO

ml → l

2.5 m = ... cm

3.4 kg = ... g

8.9 l = ... ml

Convert these into the larger units written after the dots.

There's nothing to be scared of, its easy because multiplication is the opposite of division.

× 100
CONVERT TO
m ↔ cm
100 cm in a m:
CONVERT TO
÷ 100

453 cm = __4.53__ m

379 cm = ... m

× 1000
CONVERT TO
ml ↔ l
1000 ml in a l:
CONVERT TO
÷ 1000

8500 ml = ... l

× 1000
CONVERT TO
g ↔ Kg
1000 g in a Kg:
CONVERT TO
÷ 1000

9400 g = ... kg

Change these fractions into the units written after the dots.

One quarter of a kilogram = __1000 g ÷ 4__ = __250__ g

Half a metre = ... = ... cm

One tenth of a litre = ... = ... ml

Converting Units of Area

1 square metre = __10 000__ cm².

1 square centimetre = ... mm².

Converting areas is a bit trickier.
1 sq m is 1 m by 1 m.
This is 100 cm by 100 cm.
So that's : 100 × 100 = 10 000 cm².

Measures, Shape and Space

Formulas for Measuring Shapes

Using letters in <u>formulas</u> makes them <u>quicker</u> to write out — and makes them look harder than they are. To use them, just stick <u>numbers</u> in instead of the <u>letters</u>.

Letter Formulas *for the* Perimeters *of* Rectangles

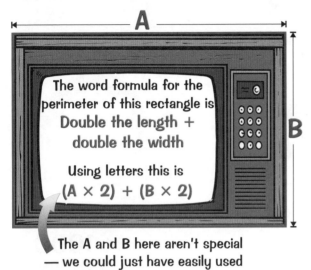

The word formula for the perimeter of this rectangle is
Double the length + double the width

Using letters this is
(A × 2) + (B × 2)

The A and B here aren't special — we could just have easily used any other letters.

This is the type of question you can work out with the formula.

What is the perimeter of the TV if side A is 50 cm and side B is 30 cm?

perimeter = (A × 2) + (B × 2)

$$= (50 \times 2) + (30 \times 2)$$

$$= 100 + 60 = 160 \ cm$$

Don't forget to put in the units at the end.

All you have to do is put 50 in instead of A and 30 in instead of B.

Then work out the sum.

What is the perimeter of the TV if side A is 100 cm and side B is 50 cm?

Perimeter = (A × 2) + (B × 2)

....

....

What is the perimeter of the TV if side A is 80 cm and side B is 60 cm?

Perimeter = (A × 2) + (B × 2)

....

....

Write out the formula for the perimeter of this rectangle using the letters shown.

....

What would be the rectangle's perimeter if M is 32 metres and G is 58 metres?

Perimeter = ...

Put your formula in here

....

....

Formulas for Measuring Shapes

Finding the Area of a Rectangle

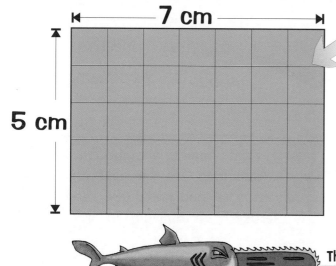

7 cm

5 cm

One way to find this rectangle's area is to count all the squares — they're all 1 cm².

There are 35 of them, so the area of the rectangle is 35 cm².

A quicker way to find the area is to use this formula:

$$\text{Area} = \text{Length} \times \text{Width}$$

$$= 7 \text{ cm} \times 5 \text{ cm} = 35 \text{ cm}^2$$

The area is given in centimetres squared — this means that 35 <u>1 cm by 1 cm squares</u> can fit into the rectangle.

Area is always measured in something squared — mm², cm², m² and km² are all measurements of area.

Using Letter Formulas

L

W

$$\text{Area} = \text{Length} \times \text{Width}$$

$$A = L \times W$$

What is the area of a rectangle that has a width of 20 mm and a length of 5 mm?

.... ← Write in the letters first.

.... ← Now fill in the numbers from the question, using the formula to help.

Writing out the formula using letters doesn't change the formula — it just makes it quicker to write down.

Use the area formula to work out the areas of these rectangles. Write the sum and the answer inside each rectangle.

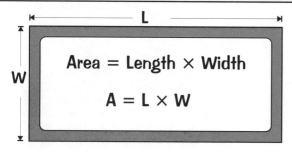

20 m

6 m

....

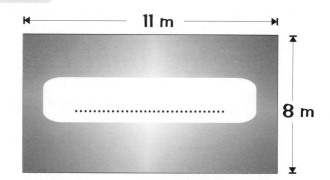

11 m

8 m

....

Bearded Gnats — you don't get much 'airier...

Area is length × width — get that right and you can't go too far wrong. The other thing to remember is to always give an area as something squared — either mm², cm², m² or km².

Measures, Shape and Space — *Estimating and Approximating*

Using the Right Units to Measure Things

Estimate the measurements below and choose the units to give your answer in.

To show that your answer is an estimate use one of these words in each answer.

Roughly   Nearly
About   Approximately

Estimate the height of your classroom.

Approximately 3 metres

First, decide what you're measuring. In this case it's distance so you know you have to choose from mm, cm, m or km.

TRY TO KEEP THE NUMBERS SMALL
In this case, instead of saying 3000 mm or 300 cm, it is better to say 3 m.

Estimate the amount of water in a fish tank.

....

Estimate the weight of a mouse.

....

Estimate the distance between your eyes.

....

What units of time would you use to measure these:

The time until your next birthday. ....

The time taken to eat your lunch. ....

The age of an old oak tree. ....

The time taken to clap your hands 20 times. ....

Apart from seconds, minutes and hours you can also use days, weeks, months and years.

Using the Right Equipment to Measure Things

What piece of equipment would you use to measure these:

The amount of liquid in a glass of milk. ....

The length of a motorway. ....

The weight of a bag of flour. ....

The distance between your eyes. ....

Estimating and Approximating

Measures, Shape and Space

Rounding Decimals to the Nearest Whole Unit

This is no different from the rounding you've already done. If the number is below halfway then you round it down. If it's exactly halfway or above you round it up.

Round these decimal measurements to the nearest whole unit.

REMEMBER to put in the units.

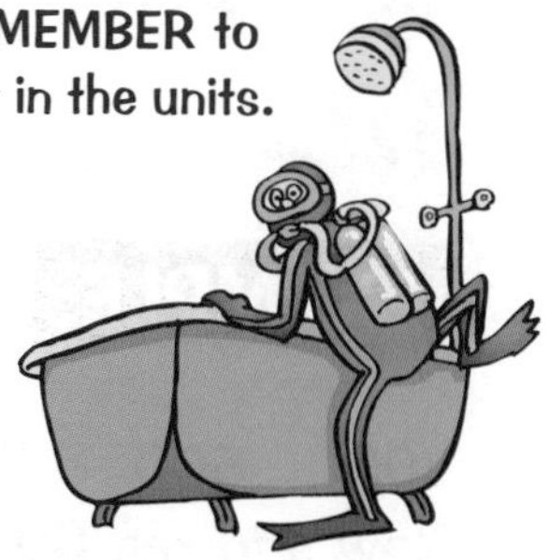

This bath has got 43.42 litres of water in it. How much is this to the nearest litre? ....

How much does a 58.55 kg punch bag weigh to the nearest kilogram? ....

Ivan — twin brother of the average monster

The twin brother of the Average Monster is 155.45 m tall. How tall is he to the nearest metre? ....

Round these measurements to the larger units given.

Be careful to look at the end units before you rush into them.

432 cm ➤ *4* .... m

5900 g ➤ .... kg

500 ml ➤ l

27 mm ➤ .... cm

7631 ml ➤ l

10 cm ➤ .... m

These ones are exactly the same, except you've got to read the units yourself.

.... cm

.... kg

Calculations	# Quick Methods for + and –

Sums with Multiples of 10 and 100

The <u>best way</u> to do sums with multiples of 10 and 100 is to <u>forget</u> the Os or OOs at the end, do the sum without them, and then <u>stick them back on</u> to the answer.

EXAMPLE: 870 – 230. First forget the Os, and you get 87 – 23 = 64. Now add the O back on to the answer.   The answer is 640.

700 + 500 + 800. First forget the OOs, and you get 7 + 5 + 8 = 20. Now add the OO back on to the answer. The answer is 2000.

Use this method to do these sums in your head.

240 + 670 = ...   800 + 700 + 300 + 600 = ...

600 + 200 + 500 = ...   550 – 330 = ...

980 – 460 = ...   400 + 900 + 200 + 700 = ...

You can use a <u>similar trick</u> when you're doing a sum with one number that <u>is a multiple of 10 or 100</u>, and another number that <u>isn't</u>. Forget about the <u>last digits</u>, do the sum, then stick the last digits back in.

EXAMPLE: 786 – 350. Forget about the units column and you get 78 – 35 = 43. Now stick that 6 from the units column on the end. The answer is 436.

With <u>multiples of 100</u>, you can forget about the <u>tens and the units</u>.

EXAMPLE: 1437 – 800. Forget both the tens and the units this time. That leaves 14 – 8 = 6. Stick that 37 from the tens and units columns back on the end. The answer is 637.

Use these methods to do these sums in your head.

769 – 420 = ...   654 – 320 = ...

1385 – 500 = ...   856 + 700 = ...

476 + 310 = ...   692 – 170 = ...

Quick Methods for + and –

Find Pairs that Add Up to Round Numbers

It's much easier to do sums when they have <u>round numbers</u> in them.
So it's really handy to be able to tell when a <u>pair of numbers</u> add up to a round number.

4.3 + 7.5 + 5.7 looks pretty <u>difficult</u>. But when you know that
<u>4.7 and 5.3 make 10</u>, it's much easier. It's simply <u>10 + 7.5 = 17.5</u>.

Each of these clouds has a pair of numbers that add up to 10. Circle them.

4.8 3.7 5.2
0.6 7.9

6.3 2.4 7.4
7.6 3.2

4.2 6.6 9.3
0.7 3.9

3.9 6.4 6.1
1.6 8.7

Look for pairs that add up to 10 to make these sums easier.

3.3 + 4.4 + 6.7 = ...   4.5 + 5.5 + 6.2 = ...

8.2 + 1.8 + 9.3 = ...   8.9 + 0.4 + 1.1 = ...

3.7 + 7.3 + 6.3 = ...   3.5 + 7.8 + 2.2 = ...

Each of these clouds has a pair of decimal fractions that add up to 1. Circle them.

0.3 0.25 0.7
0.35 0.6

0.15 0.8 0.3
0.25 0.85

0.5 0.6 0.4
0.3 0.8

0.4 0.35 0.5
0.65 0.7

Write down what decimal you would have to add to these decimals to make 1.

0.55 ....   0.1 ....   0.5 ....   0.8 ....   0.25 ....

0.05 ....   0.3 ....   0.2 ....   0.9 ....   0.65 ....

In each of these clouds, circle the pair of numbers that add up to a multiple of 100.

372 178 28
482 38

413 423 434
67 77

59 164 95
641 416

546 456 45
645 54

Column Sums with Decimals

You need to be able to add or subtract <u>decimals</u> without a <u>calculator</u>.
Easy enough — write them in <u>columns</u>, then work them out as normal.

Column Sums with Decimals — Line Them Up

EXAMPLE: What is £5.12 + £2.34?

Write the numbers in columns. Make sure the decimal points line up.

```
  £5.12
+ £2.34
```

Add the columns as normal.

When you get to the decimal points, write a new one in under the others.

```
  £5.12
+ £2.34
    .46
```

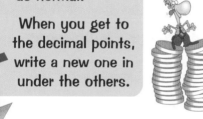

I put all my money in columns!

Then carry on adding till you've finished.

```
  £5.12
+ £2.34
  £7.46
```

That's it.
So the answer is £7.46.

Work these ones out yourself:

What is 64.3 km + 21.1 km?

```
  64.3
+ 21.1
```
.... km

Subtracting's the same — just remember the decimal point:

Work out 5.5 l – 1.2 l

```
  5.5
- 1.2
```
.... l

Decimal Sums with Carrying

When you need to <u>carry</u> or <u>borrow</u> in one of these sums, you just <u>ignore</u> the decimal point and do it anyway.

```
  2.7
+ 5.5
  8.2
   1
```

```
  ⁵6̶.¹6
-   1.9
   4.7
```

Write this in columns and then work it out:

What is 4.1 cm – 1.5 cm?

Get all the Units sorted out Before you Start

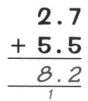

What is 2.6 m + 150 cm?
Give the answer in m.

Make sure that <u>all</u> the bits are in the <u>same units</u> — here it's either <u>cm</u> or <u>m</u>. You have to do this one in <u>m</u> because it says so.

```
  2.6
+ 1.5
  4.1
   1
```

So the answer is 4.1 m.

Real Life Fractions & Percentages

Real Life Fraction Questions are Pretty Easy

Work out the answers to these fraction questions.

There is $\frac{1}{3}$ off the cost of a tin of mustard custard.
How much do you save?

Read the question
— they <u>don't</u> want
the new price.

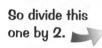

Only 66p

$66 \div 3 = 22p\ off$

To work out $\frac{1}{3}$ of the price,
just <u>divide</u> it by three.

So divide this
one by 2.

There were 12 cows here yesterday, but there are $\frac{1}{2}$ as
many more here today. How many more cows are there?

A normal jar of cheesy jam weighs 500 g.
This week the jars are $\frac{1}{10}$ bigger.
How much more does this new jar weigh?

Weisley the polar bear eats $\frac{1}{4}$ fewer fish than his mate
Bianca. She eats 32 fish, so how many fewer does he eat?

Try to Turn Real Life %s into Easy Fractions

Use any method you like to solve these ones.

Mo tried to get 20 skeletons into Rich's bedroom. She only got
75% of them in though. How many skeletons was that?

$20 \times \frac{3}{4} = 15\ skeletons$

75% is really $\frac{3}{4}$. You could
just work out $\frac{3}{4} \times 20$.

The deposit on a £200 giant sandwich is 25%.
How much is the deposit in pounds?

25% is the same as $\frac{1}{4}$.

50% of the teachers in my school come from
outer space. There are 16 teachers in my
school. How many of them are aliens?

It's normally £3.50 for a pair of monkeys,
but I have a voucher for 10% off.
How much do I save?

Making Decisions

Explain How You Solve the Problem

EXAMPLE: Harry enters the Broughton Bird Bricklaying contest. He lays bricks at the rate of 5 a minute. How long does it take him to lay 275 bricks?

ANSWER: Divide 275 by 5 to find the number of minutes. 275 ÷ 5 = 55 minutes.

Answer these sums, then explain how you did them.

Harry charges £5 an hour to lay bricks. If you had £20 to spend, how many bricks could you get Harry to lay?

....

....

Harry loses the contest to Ray, who can lay bricks at a rate of 6 a minute. How many more bricks can Ray lay in an hour?

....

....

Harry and Ray work together to build the Broughton Millennium Cone. Between them, how many bricks can they lay in a minute?

....

The Cone has 1485 bricks. How long will it take them to build?

....

Now I'll give you a sum, and you write a story that goes with it. It doesn't have to be about bricklaying birds, it can be about anything you like.

41.5 × 22 = 913

....

....

Fill in the gap in each of these sums: is it + , − , × or ÷ ?

578 .... 351 = 227   271 .... 351 = 622   912 .... 654 = 258

14 .... 7 = 98   242 .... 22 = 11   57 .... 6 = 342

Checking Results

Get an Approximate Answer by Rounding

An approximate answer is one that gives you a rough idea what the exact answer is. You change the numbers a bit so that they're easier to work out.

EXAMPLE: 603 ÷ 9 is approximately 600 ÷ 10, which is 60. The exact answer is 67 (check it on your calculator). But 600 ÷ 10 is a lot easier to work out, and it tells us the exact answer is near 60.

Round the numbers to find an approximate answer to these sums.

497 + 505 is approximately .... + ... which is ....

31 × 19 is approximately .... × .... which is ....

911 – 392 is approximately .... – .... which is ....

798 ÷ 42 is approximately .... ÷ .... which is ....

Use your calculator to check the exact answers.

Odd and Even Numbers have Certain Rules

Add an even number to an even number and you get an even number.

Add an odd number to an even number and you get an odd number.

Add an odd number to an odd number and you get an even number.

Add three odd numbers and you get an odd number.

Subtract an even number from an even number and you get an even number.

Subtract an odd number from an odd number and you get an even number.

Subtract an odd number from an even number — or an even number from an odd number — and you get an odd number.

Use the rules to say if the answers to these questions are odd or even.

572 – 419 is *Odd* ....   142 + 556 is *Even* ....

290 – 182 is ....   517 + 233 is ....

863 – 236 is ....   316 + 349 is ....

909 – 281 is ....   297 + 423 is ....

715 – 326 is ....   726 + 511 is ....

643 – 279 is ....   206 + 884 is ....

889 – 464 is ....   97 + 113 + 327 is ....

Numbers and the Number System

Square Numbers

Here's something new. You've heard of <u>odd</u> numbers, <u>even</u> numbers, and <u>negative</u> numbers. Well, (hold your breath) these are SQUARE numbers!

They're called Square numbers because...

... you can make squares out of them.

$1 \times 1 = 1$ $2 \times 2 = 4$ $3 \times 3 = 9$ $4 \times 4 = 16$ $5 \times 5 = 25$

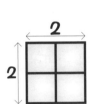 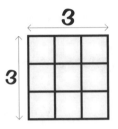 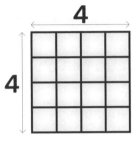 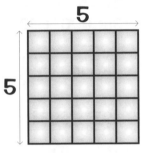

1 squared = 1

2 squared = 4

3 squared = 9

4 squared = 16

5 squared = 25

Any number squared is just that number times itself.

$2 \text{ squared} = 2 \times 2 = 4$

Work out the answers to these questions.

What is 1 squared? ....   What's 5 squared? ....

Is 20 a square number? ....   What is the square of 3? ....

This means "can you get 20 by squaring a number?"

This just means "What is 3 squared?"

A Little "2" means squared

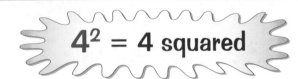

$4^2 = 4 \text{ squared}$

I said, "eat three square meals", not three square numbers!

Find the answers to these.

Work out 4^2. ....   Work out 5^2. ....   What's another way to write "3 squared"? ....

Fill these in. $1^2 =$ .... $\ldots^2 = 4$ $10^2 =$ ....

$\ldots^2 = 25$ $4^2 = $........ $\ldots^2 = 9$ $\ldots^2 = 36$

Square Numbers

Learn All the Square Numbers up to 10^2

You have to know <u>all</u> the square numbers up to $\underline{10}^2$ — here are the rest of them.

$6^2 = 6 \times 6$
$\quad\ = 36$

$7^2 = 7 \times 7$
$\quad\ = 49$

$8^2 = 8 \times 8$
$\quad\ = 64$

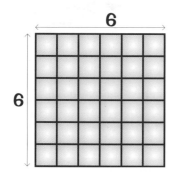

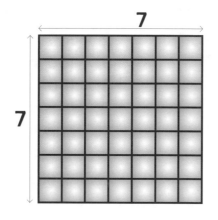

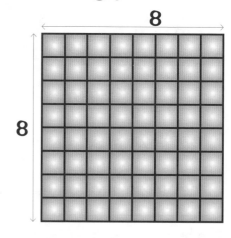

$9^2 = 9 \times 9$
$\quad\ = 81$

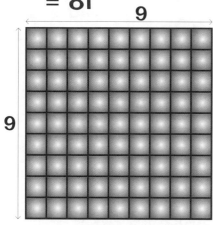

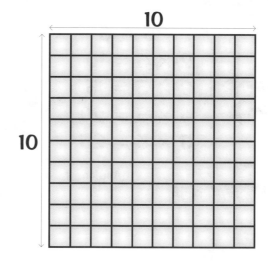

$10^2 = 10 \times 10$
$\qquad\ = 100$

Fill in the answers to these questions.

This is just 7^2 in disguise. Don't forget to give the answer in cm^2.

What is 6^2? ....

What number multiplied by itself gives 64?
....

Is 52 a square number?
....

What is the area of a square whose sides are 7 cm long? ....

Write out all the square numbers up to 100.

....

....

No, that's a square <u>plumber</u>.

Frightened? — It's Square-y stuff...

Don't forget "Squared" means "times by itself" — and that little 2 means squared as well.

Numbers and the Number System

Spot the Divisible Number

Here's how you spot if a number can be <u>divided</u> by <u>2</u>, <u>4</u>, <u>5</u>, <u>10</u> or <u>100</u>.

I prefer invisible numbers!

Seeing if it will Divide by 2, 4, 5, 10 or 100

The quickest way is to <u>look at the last digits</u>.

Here's the <u>10 times table</u>.

$1 \times 10 = 10$
$2 \times 10 = 20$
$3 \times 10 = 30$
$4 \times 10 = 40$

(And on and on...)

If it's got 0 on the end, it'll divide by 10.

| Is 72 divisible by 10? | .... |

| Does 10 go into 7540? | .... |

Here's the <u>100 times table</u>.

$1 \times 100 = 100$
$2 \times 100 = 200$
$3 \times 100 = 300$
$4 \times 100 = 400$
$5 \times 100 = 500$

(And on and on, yawn...)

If it's got 00 on the end, it'll divide by 100.

| Can 600 be divided by 100? | .... |

| Does 100 go into 607? | .... |

And here's the <u>5 times table</u>.

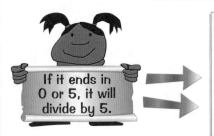

If it ends in 0 or 5, it will divide by 5.

$1 \times 5 = 5$
$2 \times 5 = 10$
$3 \times 5 = 15$
$4 \times 5 = 20$
$5 \times 5 = 25$

(And on...)

| Can 45 be shared between 5? | .... |

| Does 5 go into 385? | .... |

I'm sure you can all remember the <u>2 times table</u>...

If it ends in 0, 2, 4, 6 or 8, it will divide by 2.

$10 \times 2 = 20$
$11 \times 2 = 22$
$12 \times 2 = 24$
$13 \times 2 = 26$
$14 \times 2 = 28$
$15 \times 2 = 30$

| Can 133 be divided by 2? | .... |

| Is 8836 divisible by 2? | .... |

You can see if a number will divide by 4 <u>without dividing the whole thing by 4</u>.

If the last two digits divide by 4, the number divides by 4.

If a year can be divided by 4, then it's a leap year. Was 1924 a leap year?

$1924 = 1900 + 24$

Ignore the blue bits — 100 divides by 4, so any number of hundreds (or thousands or whatever) will too.

Only the last two digits are important.

24 is a multiple of 4, so the answer's <u>yes</u>.

So, you have a go:

| Will 108 divide by 4? | | Will 3812 divide by 4? | | Will 4646 divide by 4? |

....

Reasoning About Numbers

Just Try it and See if the Statement is True

Sometimes you see a statement and you don't know if it's true.
You might be able to tell by trying out some examples.

EXAMPLE:

A multiple of 8 is always twice a multiple of 4.

Squawk!

24 is 3 × 8

Try one out to see if it's true.

24 = 12 × 2, and 12 is a multiple of 4.

The perimeter of a rectangle is
(length of longest side + length of shortest side) × 2.

Just try any rectangle and write out the sum to see
if it's true.

....

If you swap the 2 numbers round in a subtraction sum, the answer is not the same.

Check it out!

Just choose any numbers and write
out the sum to show it's true.

....

The angles in a triangle always add up to 180°.

Try it out — draw a triangle in this space
and measure the angles of the corners.

Write the angle
sum in here.

....

Nasty blob of goo.

The sum of two odd numbers is .

I can't see if it should
say "odd" or "even".

You can work this out in the same way. Try it with any
two odd numbers, and see if the answer's odd or even.

Write out the whole statement here.

....

....

....

Boiled, fried or poached? — Try An Egg Sample ...

Statements are important in maths — it's always a good idea to try an example to help
you understand the statement and check there's no mistake.

Reasoning About Numbers

Some Questions ask for Answers in Words

Explain how to find the number of days in any number of weeks.

There are 7 days in 1 week,
14 days in 2 weeks,
21 days in 3 weeks...

There's a pattern here — it's the number of weeks × 7.

Take the number of weeks and multiply by seven.

Write it out clearly, in words.

Explain how to find out the number of banana shoes left over if some people take a pair each from a box of 26.

Each person takes 2 shoes, so...

Double the number of people, and take it away from 26.

My machine takes a number, doubles it and then takes away 2. It starts with 3 and I feed each number back in when it comes out. Write down the first 5 numbers in the sequence.

This is easier — no words to write.

Describe a way to calculate the perimeter of a rectangle.

You know how to do this, so think how to say it clearly in words.

Tony is number jumping. He jumps over 1, then 2, then 4, then 8, then 16, ... What's the rule?

You should think about what you have to do to get to the <u>next</u> number.

Answers: Pages 1 – 9

Page 1 — Money & Decimals on Calculators

"Fill in the calculator buttons that you need to press..."
£2.54 + £9.27 = **£12.81**   PRESS: 2 . 5 4 + **9** : **6 7** =
£6.99 – £4.59 = **£2.40**   PRESS: **6** : **9 9 – 4** : **5 9 =**

"Fill in the missing number in the sum below."
5.27 – **3.59** = 1.68   WORKING: **5.27 – 1.68 = 3.59**

"1086 were made. How many had the fault?"
1086 ÷ 3 = **362**

"How many weeks will it take him to get all the money..."
156 ÷ 1.50 = **104**

"Check your answer."   **104 × 1.50 = 156**

Page 2 — Basic Shapes

"Draw the two diagonals on this rectangle."

"Measure the length of each side and write in the results below."
Side A = **41** or **42mm**   Side C = **41** or **42mm**
Side B = **32mm**   Side D = **32mm**
An angle of 90° is called a **right angle.**

"Say why each of these shapes is NOT a rectangle."
Opposite sides are not parallel, angles are not right angles.
Shape has more than 4 sides.
Opposite sides are not equal length, angles are not 90°.

"Choose the right words from underneath..."
All four angles are **right angles**.
Opposite sides are **equal** and **parallel**.

Page 3 — Basic Shapes

"Measure the lengths of the sides and the sizes of the angles..."

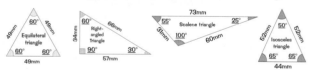

"Put the triangle names in the sentences below."
An **isosceles** triangle has two equal...
In a **right-angled** triangle one of the angles...
In an **equilateral** triangle all three sides are...
In a **scalene** triangle no two sides or angles...

"Fill in all of their triangle names and then circle the one..."
equilateral   **isosceles**   **scalene**   **right-angled**

Page 4 — Symmetry in Polygons

"Use the mirror method to draw the lines of symmetry on..."

"Trace these shapes onto a blank piece of paper. Use the..."

6 lines of s.   **7** lines of s.   **8** lines of s.   **5** lines of s.
6 sides   **7** sides   **8** sides   **5** sides

"Fill in the lines beneath each shape. Write a rule about the..."
The number of lines of symmetry equals the number of sides.

Page 5 — Symmetrical Patterns

"A and B have been done, but it's up to you to do C and D."

"Complete these symmetrical patterns in the..."

Page 6 — Parallel and Perpendicular

"Write under each set of lines whether they are parallel..."
perpendicular   **neither**   **perpendicular**   **parallel**

"Write down the parallel sides of this square..."
Parallel sides of square: **a** & **c**   **b** & **d**
Perpendicular sides of octagon:
a & **c**   **a** & **g**   **c** & **e**   **e** & **g**   **h** & **b**   **h** & **f**   **d** & **b**   **d** & **f**

Page 7 — Diagonals

"Draw all the diagonals on these regular polygons..."

No. sides = **5**   No. sides = **6**   No. sides = **7**
No. diag. = **5**   No. diag. = **9**   No. diag. = **14**

"Fill in the information below."
Tessa's shell has **8** sides and **20** diagonals.

Page 8 — Acute and Obtuse Angles

"Fill in the blanks below with either 90° or 180°."
Right angles are always **90°**.
An angle twice the size of a right angle is **180°**.
An angle less than **90°** is acute.
An angle between **90°** and **180°** is obtuse.

"Write beneath each of these angles whether they are acute..."

Right angles	Obtuse
Acute	**Acute**
	Obtuse
Acute	**Obtuse**

"Draw a match in each picture to show; a) a right angle..."
b) Any suitable, eg   **c) Any suitable, eg**

Page 9 — Reasoning about Shapes

"Count all the possible rectangles in this picture."

9	**6**	**3**
6	**4**	**2**
3	**2**	**1** Total = **36**

Answers: Pages 9 – 20

"Count all the triangles in this picture."
Total = **13**

Page 10 — Perimeter Formulas

"What is the perimeter of a rectangle if its long side is 20cm..."
$2 \times \underline{\textbf{20}} + 2 \times \underline{\textbf{5}} = \underline{\textbf{40}} + \underline{\textbf{10}} = \underline{\textbf{50}}$

"Work out the perimeters of the rectangles below."
$\underline{\textbf{2} \times \textbf{56} + \textbf{2} \times \textbf{22} = \textbf{112} + \textbf{44} = \textbf{156}}$
$\underline{\textbf{2} \times \textbf{42} + \textbf{2} \times \textbf{20} = \textbf{84} + \textbf{40} = \textbf{124}}$

"Complete this formula for the perimeter of a pentagon."
The length of a side $\times$ **5** = the perimeter of a pentagon.

"Make up a formula for working out the perimeter of any..."
The length of a side $\times$ the number of sides = the perimeter.

Page 11 — Measuring Area

"Work out the areas of the rectangles below."
$12 \times 8 = \underline{\textbf{96cm}^2}$ $6 \times 2 = \underline{\textbf{12mm}^2}$ $14 \times 20 = \underline{\textbf{280m}^2}$

"Write in whether you would use mm^2, cm^2 or m^2..."
A car park **m^2**
This page **cm^2**
A fingernail **mm^2**
A tennis court **m^2**
A birthday card **cm^2**
A shirt button **mm^2**
The side of a brick **cm^2**
The top of a calculator **cm^2**
A caterpillar's rucksack **mm^2**
The floor in the classroom **m^2**

Page 12 — Understanding Units and Scales

"Work out these conversions using 1 pint = 570ml."
10 pints = **5700 ml**   3 pints = **1710 ml**   1140 ml = **2 pints**

"Work out these conversions using 1 mile = 1600 m."
2 miles = **3200 m**   1/2 mile = **800 m**   16 000 m = **10 miles**

"Work out these conversions using 1 gallon = 5 l."
4 gallons = **20 l**   10 gallons = **50 l**   200 litres = **40 gallons**

"The Average Monster has 15 pints of blood. How much..."
8550 ml

Page 13 — Understanding Units and Scales

"What are the distance between the arrows below?"
$64 - 37 = \underline{\textbf{27 mm}}$

$850 - 350 = \underline{\textbf{500 ml}}$ $670 - 320 = \underline{\textbf{350 ml}}$

"If Nigel drinks 200 ml of gunk from the beaker below..."
$350 - 200 = \underline{\textbf{150 ml}}$
"If 250 grams of green goo is taken off the scales how much..."
$470 - 250 = \underline{\textbf{220 g}}$

Page 14 — Time and the 24-Hour Clock

"Change these times into 24 hour clock times."
Six thirty in the morning = **6:30 am** = **06:30**
Five fifteen in the evening = **5:30 pm** = **17:30**
Eleven twenty-nine at night = **11:29 pm** = **23:29**

"Conan knows that at 9.23 pm he must put his gas mask on..."
21:23

Page 15 — Timetables

"Use the timetable above to answer these questions."
12:30
The 11:15
3 stations
2 hrs 40 mins
"Otto's train was delayed due to invisible ants on the track..."
The **13:55** from Dugong.

Page 16 — Probability Scales

"Say whether these things are likely, unlikely, certain..."
Certain
Unlikely
Certain
Impossible

"Join each balloon to the person in the right place on the line."

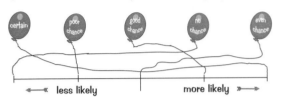

less likely   more likely

Page 17 — Using Data to Check Results

"Number of odd numbers rolled." **Depends on experiment.**

"Number of even numbers rolled." **Depends on experiment.**

"Does your data agree with Neil's prediction?"
If more even numbers were rolled — yes. If more odd — no.

"If you did the experiment again, do you think..."
No, because it depends on random chance.

"How many games did Lenny play?"
17

"What was the mode of Lenny's scores?"
3

"In how many games did Lenny score 2 or more?"
12

Page 18 — Mental Strategies for + and –

"Try these sums by finding pairs that add up to 10."
$\underline{\textbf{40}} + 18 = \underline{\textbf{58}}$
$\underline{\textbf{60}} + 45 = \underline{\textbf{105}}$
$\underline{\textbf{13}} + 30 = \underline{\textbf{43}}$

"Now do these sums starting off with the largest number."
$\underline{\textbf{54}} + \textbf{25} + 23 = \underline{\textbf{79}} + 23 = \underline{\textbf{102}}$
$\underline{\textbf{90}} + \textbf{16} + 9 = \underline{\textbf{106}} + 9 = \underline{\textbf{115}}$
$\underline{\textbf{88}} + \textbf{22} + 7 = \underline{\textbf{110}} + 7 = \underline{\textbf{117}}$

Page 19 — Mental Strategies for + and –

"257 + 364 = 621. Write 3 other statements from this sum."
364 + 257 = 621   621 – 364 = 257   621 – 257 = 364

"624 + 164 = 788. Write down the answers to these ..."
$788 - 164 = \underline{\textbf{624}}$ $788 - 624 = \underline{\textbf{164}}$ $164 + 624 = \underline{\textbf{788}}$

"Use the numbers 356, 81, 456, 437, 275, 100 and 256 to..."
356 – 256 = 100   100 + 256 = 356   256 + 100 = 356
456 – 100 = 356   456 – 356 = 100   100 + 356 = 456
356 + 100 = 456   356 – 256 = 100   100 + 256 = 356
256 + 100 = 356   275 + 81 = 356   81 + 275 = 356
356 – 81 = 275   356 – 275 = 81   356 + 81 = 437
81 + 356 = 437   437 – 356 = 81   437 – 81 = 356

Page 20 — Mental Strategies for + and –

"Find a multiplication that is the same as each..."
$29 + 30 + 31 = \underline{\textbf{30}} \times \textbf{3} = \underline{\textbf{90}}$
$36 + 40 + 44 = \underline{\textbf{40}} \times \textbf{3} = \underline{\textbf{120}}$
$40 + 41 + 39 = \underline{\textbf{40}} \times \textbf{3} = \underline{\textbf{120}}$
$10 + 6 + 12 + 14 + 8 = \underline{\textbf{10}} \times \textbf{5} = \underline{\textbf{50}}$

Answers: Pages 21 – 31

Page 21 — Column Sums with Big Numbers

"Add up these numbers. Don't forget to carry if you…"
4560   **4074**   **9938**

"Use the compensation method to solve these subtractions."
2368   **4580**   **3866**

"Try these."
7329   **5545**   **5583**

Page 22 — Money and Real Life Problems

"Professor Plank bought 2 balloons. One cost £3.40…"
£1.82

"How much money does he have now?"
£4.36

"Seb Bootio has been playing for 17 minutes of a football…"
28

"Simon has five 1p coins, three 2p coins, four 5p coins…"
20 + 10 + 10 + 10   **20 + 10 + 10 + 5 + 5**   **20 + 10 + 5 + 5 + 5 + 5**
20 + 10 + 5 + 5 + 2 + 2 + 1   **20 + 10 + 5 + 5 + 1 + 1 + 1 + 1**
10 + 10 + 10 + 5 + 5 + 5 + 5   **10 + 10 + 10 + 5 + 5 + 5 + 2 + 2 + 1**
10 + 10 + 10 + 5 + 5 + 5 + 1 + 1 + 1 + 1 + 1

Page 23 — Money and Real Life Problems

"How far has Jake left to swim?"
One sixth

"How many meatballs has she got altogether?"
240

"How many 50p packets of sauce can Tom Meatball buy…"
8

"What time did Rosemary finish eating?"
12:20pm

Page 24 — Making Decisions

"I'm sure you could do a sum like 43 + 6 in your head…"
49

"…but you might need to do 43 + 98 on paper:"
141

"I would understand if you needed a calculator to work out…"
4214

"Decide how to do these questions, then solve them…"
54   Method: **In head**
680   Method: **Calculator**
1146   Method: **Paper**
59   Method: **Paper**
384   Method: **Paper**

Page 25 — Checking Results

"Solve these additions and subtractions and check them with…"
656   Check: **656** – 375 = 281
632   Check: **632** + **614** = **1246**
1489   Check: **1489** – **934** = **555** OR **1489** – **555** = **934**

"Now have a go at these multiplications and divisions, and…"
43   Check: **43** × **30** = **1320**
920   Check: **920** ÷ **20** = **46** OR **920** ÷ **46** = **20**
36   Check: **36** × **51** = **1836**

Page 26 — Properties of Numbers

"Complete these number sequences."
2, 5, **8**, **11**, **14**, **17**, 20
6, 11, 16, **21**, **26**, **31**, 36
40, 34, 28, **22**, **16**, **10**, 4
"Fill in the next four terms in these sequences."
4.2, 6.2, 8.2, **10.2**, **12.2**, **14.2**, **16.2**
5.5, 5, 4.5, **4**, **3.5**, **3**, **2.5**
3.6, 4.2, 4.8, **5.4**, **6**, **6.6**, **7.2**
"Fill in the next four terms in these sequences."
−4, −8, −12, **−16**, **−20**, **−24**, **−28**
9, 6, 3, **0**, **−3**, **−6**, **−9**
−27, −20, −13, **−6**, **1**, **8**, **15**

Page 27 — Properties of Numbers

"Circle the numbers that have a factor of 6."
24   **6**   **30**   **42**

"This time see if you can circle the factors of the number 64."
2   **64**   **1**   **32**   **16**   **4**
"List all the factors of these numbers."
7 and **1**
14, **7**, **2** and **1**
30, **15**, **10**, **6**, **5**, **3**, **2**, and **1**

Page 28 — Reasoning About Numbers

"Find three consecutive numbers which have a product of:"
24: **2 × 3 × 4**   210: **5 × 6 × 7**

"Find as many ways as you can of making 1000 by adding…"
889 + 111   **732 + 268**   **458 + 431 + 111**
190 + 170 + 640   **190 + 111 + 431 + 268**

"Find ways to complete this sum by putting in numbers…"
1 + 1 + 3   **1 + 2 + 2**   **0 + 1 + 4**   **0 + 2 + 3**

"Each tortoise stands for a missing number in this problem…"
42 × **51** = 2142

Page 29 — Place Value

"Write in these missing numbers by working them out in…"
230   **100**
60   **76**
10   **4700**
8   **10**

Page 30 — Proportion

"Estimate the positions of the worms on these number lines."
About **750**   About **−16**

"Estimate the amount of milk left in the bottle below…"
About **a third** (it's actually two sevenths)

"Draw a mark $\frac{1}{5}$ of the way up the tree trunk…"

Page 31 — Temperature Difference

"What temperature does this thermometer show?"
22 °C

"How about this one?"
−3 °C

"By how many degrees must the temperature fall before he…"
17 °C

"The temperature this morning was −9 °C, and has…"
12 °C

77

ANSWERS

Answers: Pages 31 – 41

"What is the temperature difference between the towns?"
33 °C

"What temperature is that?"
4 °C

Page 32 — Using Calculators

"Draw arrows to show which buttons do these things."

Make negative: +/− Square root: √

At end of calculation: = Clear last number: c

"How many portions can he sell?"
40

"If he sold them all for 85p each how much will he make?"
£34

"How much money did Charlie make altogether?"
£24

"Use a calculator to answer these questions..."
20

"Now try these ones..."
41   **−14**   **96**

Page 33 — Understanding Division

"See how quickly you can answer these division questions:"
... 56 by 7 = **8**   ... of 6 in 48 = **8**
... factors of 36 = **1** , **2** , **3** , **4** , **6** , **9** , **12** , **18**
... 8 between 48 = **6**   ... divisible by 6? **yes**

"How many bits will he make if he chops them into 12 cm bits?"
25

"Fill in these blanks."

9	**3**	**72**
43	**1890**	**3**

Page 34 — Understanding Division

"Do these divisions and write the answers as fractions."

$8\frac{1}{4}$ $5\frac{5}{6}$ $6\frac{1}{3}$ $5\frac{6}{7}$

"Do these divisions and write the answers as decimals."
9.1   **9.2**   **14.5**   **8.5**

Page 35 — Mental Strategies for × and ÷

"Try these sums using halving and doubling sums:"
106 chillies   **49** golf balls   **178** socks   **156** ice cubes

"Use these tricks to answer these questions."

490	**816**
270	**276**

"Travis needs to help to double up his baking orders. Use..."
$2 \times 25 =$ **50** $4 \times 25 = 100$
$8 \times 25 =$ **200** $16 \times 25 =$ **400**

Page 36 — Mental Strategies for × and ÷

"Double a fraction — the bottom gets smaller."

25	**45**
75	**125**
20	**50**

"Use factors to answer these."

104	**15**
294	**25**
105	**6**

Page 37 — Multiplication Methods

"Use the grid method to do these multiplications."

6	400	90	3
	2400	540	18

= **2958**

7	200	50	1
	1400	350	7

= **1757**

4	800	30	4
	3200	120	16

= **3336**

"Use the same method with these slightly bigger numbers."

	70	2
30	2100	60
8	560	16

= **2836**

	90	8
50	4500	400
4	360	32

= **5292**

"36 × 27 ="   **720 + 252 = 972**
"342 × 9 ="   **2700 + 360 + 18 = 3078**

Page 38 — Money and Real Life Problems

"How much did she spend altogether?"
£29.06

"How much will it cost her to fill up her five litre can?"
£3.21

"How much has she saved?"
£44.20

"What different amounts could she pay for with these stamps?"
25 + 25 + 35 + 35 = £1.20   **25 + 25 + 35 = 85p**
25 + 35 + 35 = 95p   **25 + 35 = 60p**   **25p**   **35p**

"How many pesetas, francs and dollars will she get for £5?"
£5 = 43.5 francs = 8 Sorcerer's Dollars

Page 39 — Number Stories & Decisions

"Make up your own number stories for these sums."
1435 + 3245 = 4680
Any suitable, e.g. I ate 1435 hot dogs on Saturday, and 3245 on Sunday, so I ate 4680 in the whole weekend.

38.7 × 24 = 928.8
Any suitable, e.g. I have to pay £38.70 each time I break the diving board. I broke it 24 times today, so that's £928.8 in total.

564 ÷ 8 = 70.5
Any suitable, e.g. 546 cakes shared between 8 people is 70.5 each.

"Fill in the right signs in these sums."
319 **+** 274 = 593   18 **×** 6 = 108
572 **−** 291 = 281   572 **+** 291 = 863
19 **×** 52 = 988   228 **÷** 38 = 6

Page 40 — Approximating Sums

"Estimate these by rounding first and then work them out."

Estimate:		Answer:	
420 + 110 = 530		530	
20 × 10 = 200		189	
590 − 210 = 380		371	
500 ÷ 100 = 4.9		5	
820 − 390 = 430		432	

Page 41 – Fractions

"Use this method to work out these."

$20 \times \frac{3}{4} = \frac{60}{4} = $ **15**, $20 \times \frac{4}{10} = \frac{80}{10} = $ **8**, $50 \times \frac{2}{10} = \frac{100}{10} = $ **10**

"What is the difference between the weights Dave..."

$18 \times \frac{2}{3} = \frac{36}{3} = $ **12 kg**

Answers: Pages 42 – 52

Page 42 — Decimals

"Use the same method to solve these mixed unit questions."
500 cm + 60 cm = **560 cm**   10 m + 4000 m = **4010 m**
3000 g – 1500 g = **1500 g**   150mm – 20 mm = **130 mm**
4000 m – 15 m = **3985 m**

Page 43 — Percentages

"Write these fractions as percentages."
salt: **15** %   fizz: **45** %   custard: **87** %

Page 44 — Percentages

"Work out these percentages using the method above."
50 % of 200 = 50 × 2 = **100**
30 % of 500 = 30 × 5 = **150**
15 % of 300 = 15 × 3 = **45**
75 % of 200 = 75 × 2 = **150**
20 % of 50 = 20 × $\frac{1}{2}$ = **10**

Page 45 — Percentages

"Work out the shaded fraction and percentage of each shape."
Circle: $\frac{3}{4}$ = 75 %   Square: $\frac{1}{4}$ = 25 %
3 × 2 Rectangle: $\frac{1}{2}$ = 50 %
5 × 2 Rectangle: $\frac{1}{10}$ = 10 %

Page 46 — Percentages

"Fill in the missing fractions and percentages, just to show..."
50 % = $\frac{1}{2}$ $\frac{1}{4}$ = **25 %** $\frac{3}{4}$ = **75 %**   10 % = $\frac{1}{10}$

"Try these for size, using the new method:"
50% of 38 = **19**   25% of 88 = **22**   10% of 140 = **14**
75% of 64 = **58**   60% of 40 = **24**   90% of 50 = **45**

Page 47 — Ration and Proportion

"Garry put 6 eggs in. How many daffodils does he need?"
18

"Matt and Nic use the same recipe. They put 18..."
6

"Tim chooses 4 songs. How many tunes does Garry choose?"
10

"Garry picks 35 songs. How many choices does Tim..."
14

"Yesterday Tim picked 6 songs. How many songs did..."
Garry must have picked 15 songs, so total = **21**

Page 48 — Organising and Interpreting Data

"Fill in the table with all the scores and answer the questions."

Name	Frog Flipping Score (out of 10)	Shabby Shot Score (out of 10)
Allie	9	6
Steven	9	2
Chuck	9	8
Bertie	8	9
Polly	9	6
Frannie	7	6

Most common score: Frog Flipping — **9**
                    Shabby Shot — **6**

Maximum score: Frog Flipping — **9**
                    Shabby Shot — **9**

Minimum score: Frog Flipping — **7**
                    Shabby Shot — **2**

Difference between highest and lowest scores:
Frog Flipping — **2**   Shabby Shot — **7**

Page 49 — Probability

"How many matches did Barrow play in?"
4 + 1 + 6 + 3 + 4 + 2 = **20**

"What was the maximum number of goals Barrow scored..."
5

"In how many of their matches did Barrow score MORE..."
6

"What was the MODE — the most common number of..."
2

"How likely are Barrow to score 7 goals in a match next..."
Unlikely

Page 50 — Plotting Line Graphs

"Practise again with plotting the points and drawing a line..."

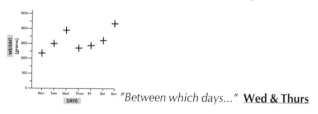

"Between which days..." **Wed & Thurs**

Page 51 — Using a Calculator

"What would you round these numbers up to?"
7.9999999 = **8**
144.9999999 = **145**   23.9999999 = **24**
58.9999999 = **60**   99.9999999 = **100**

"Write down the two closest whole numbers that these..."
91.55 is between **91** and **92**   16.493 is between **16** and **17**
212.74 is between **212** and **213**   0.25 is between **0** and **1**

"How many feathers does she use for one clip?..."
233.33 ÷ 100 = **2.3333**   is between **2** and **3**

"How many feathers does she use for three clips?..."
2.3333 × 3 = 6.9999 = **7** to the nearest whole number

Page 52 — Reflection

"Does a square have reflective symmetry?"   **Yes**

"Draw two more lines of symmetry on the square."

"Finish drawing these shapes and work out whether they..."

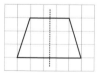

1 line of symm.   **2** lines of symm.   **No** lines of symm.

"Draw a reflection of William's footprint across the mirror..."

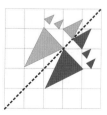

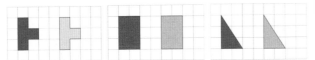

Page 53 — Translation

"Translate these shapes four units to the right and draw…"

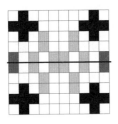

"It's time to use translation and reflection together to create…"

Page 54 — Directions and Grid Positions

"Mark these points on the map of the kitchen and draw…"

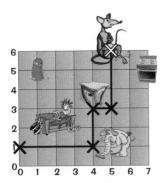

"Finish off the directions for her."
Go forward 4 units before you hit Milly. Turn left and go forward **two units before you hit the table. Turn right and go forward one unit. Turn left, and go forward 3 units until you get to the cheeky rat.**

"Write down the points where the robot has to turn."
Any suitable, e.g. (5, 6), (3, 6), (3, 4), (0, 4), (0, 1).

Page 55 — Directions and Grid Positions

"Write down the co-ordinates of the 4 points on this grid."
(0, 3) (1, 1) (3, 4) (4, 2)

"What shape do the points make?"
A parallelogram

"Plot the points (1, 1), (3, 1)…"

"What shape do they make?" Any suitable, e.g. house/pencil

Page 56 — Calculating Angles

"Estimate the size of these angles, to the nearest 5°."
25° ± 5°   **145°** ± 5°   **80°** ± 5°

"Now measure these angles."
Clockwise from left: **55°   110°   130°   10°**

Page 57 — Calculating Angles

"Use a protractor to draw these angles:"

"What sizes are these angles?"
Top: $180° - 82° = $ **98°**   Bottom: $180° - 115° = $ **65°**

Page 58 — Investigating Numbers & Shapes

"Use examples to investigate this rule."
Square: measured = **112mm**   Pentagon: meas'd = **130mm**
          calculated = **112mm**   calc'd = **130mm**

Hexagon: meas'd = **126mm**   Octagon: meas'd = **122mm**
          calculated = **112mm**   calc'd = **130mm**

"Use examples to investigate this rule."
Any of: $9 × 1 = 9$ $9 × 2 = 18$, $1 + 8 = 9$
          $9 × 3 = 26$, $2 + 6 = 9$ $9 × 4 = 36$, $3 + 6 = 9$
          $9 × 5 = 45$, $4 + 5 = 9$ $9 × 6 = 54$, $5 + 4 = 9$
          $9 × 7 = 63$, $6 + 3 = 9$ $9 × 8 = 72$, $7 + 2 = 9$
          $9 × 9 = 81$, $8 + 1 = 9$

Page 59 — Converting Units

"Convert these into the smaller units written after the dots."
5.1 kg = **5100** g   7.2 l = **7200** ml   2.5 m = **250** cm
3.4 kg = **3400** g   8.9 l = **8900** ml

"Convert these into the larger units written after the dots."
379 cm = **3.79** m   8500 ml = **8.5** l   9400 g = **9.4** kg

"Change these fractions into the units written after the dots."
Half a metre = **0.5** m = **50** cm
One tenth of a litre = **0.1** l = **100** ml

"Converting units of area"
1 square centimetre = **100** mm^2

Page 60 — Formulas for Measuring Shapes

"What is the perimeter of TV if side A is 100 cm and…"
$(100 × 2) + (50 × 2) = 200 + 100 = $ 300 cm

"What is the perimeter of TV if side A is 80 cm and…"
$(80 × 2) + (60 × 2) = 160 + 120 = $ 280 cm

"Write out the formula for the perimeter of this rectangle…"
Perimeter $= (M × 2) + (G × 2)$

"What would be the rectangle's perimeter if M is 32 metres…"
$(32 × 2) + (58 × 2) = 64 + 116 = $ 180 m

Page 61 — Formulas for Measuring Shapes

"What is the area of a rectangle that has a width of 20mm…"
$A = L × W = 5 × 20 = $ 100 mm^2

"Use the area formula to work out the area of these…"
    $20 × 6 = $ **120 m^2** $11 × 8 = $ **88 m^2**

Page 62 — Estimating and Approximating

"Estimate the measurements below and choose the units…"
Water in fish tank: any reasonable answer, e.g. 5 l to 100 l
Weight of mouse: any reasonable answer, e.g. 10 g to 50 g
Distance between eyes: any reasonable answer, e.g. 2cm

Answers: Pages 62 – 72

"What units of time would you use to measure these:"
Time till birthday – **months**   Time to eat lunch – **minutes**
Age of oak tree – **years**   Time to clap – **seconds**

"What piece of equipment would you use to measure these:"
Amount of liquid in glass – **measuring jug**
Length of m'way – **a really big tape measure**, or **map and string**
Weight of bag of flour – **measuring scales** or **balance**
Distance between eyes – **ruler**

Page 63 — Estimating and Approximating

"This bath has got 43.42 litres of water..."   **43 l**

"How much does a 58.55 kg punch..."   **59 kg**

"The twin brother of the Average Monster..."   **155 m**

"Round these measurements to the larger units given."
    5900 g: **6** kg   500 ml: **1** l   27 mm: **3** cm
    7631 ml: **8** l   10 cm: **0** m

"These ones are the exactly the same, except you've got to..."
Ant house: **3** cm   Cowboy and Horse: **500** kg

Page 64 — Quick Methods for + and –

"Use this method to do these sums in your head."
    910   **2400**
      1300   **220**
    520   **2200**

"Use these methods to do these sums in your head."
    349   **334**
    885   **1556**
    786   **862**

Page 65 — Quick Methods for + and –

"Each of these clouds has a pair of numbers..."
    4.8 + **5.2**   **2.4** + **7.6**   **0.7** + **9.3**   **6.1** + **3.9**

"Look for pairs that add up to 10 to make..."
    14.4   **16.2**
    19.3   **10.4**
    17.3   **13.5**

"Each of these clouds has a pair of decimal fractions that..."
    0.7 + **0.3**   **0.15** + **0.85**   **0.4** + **0.6**   **0.35** + **0.65**

"Write down what decimal you would have to add..."
    0.55 + **0.45**   0.05 + **0.95**   0.1 + **0.9**   0.3 + **0.7**
    0.5 + **0.5**   0.2 + **0.8**   0.8 + **0.2**   0.9 + **0.1**
    0.25 + **0.75**   0.65 + **0.35**

"In each of these clouds, circle the pair of numbers that..."
    372 + 28   **423 + 77**   **641 + 59**   **546 + 54**

Page 66 — Column Sums with Decimals

"What is 64.3 km + 21.2 km?"   **85.4 km**

"Work out 5.5 l – 1.2 l"   **4.3 l** $\overset{3}{4}.\overset{}{1}$
                                                                              $-\ 1.5$
                    "What is 4.1cm – 1.5 cm?"   **2.6**

Page 67 — Real Life Fractions and Percentages

"There were 12 cows here yesterday, but..."   **6 more**

"A normal jar of cheesy jam weighs 500 g..."   **550 g**

"Weisley the polar bear eats..."   **8 fewer**

"The deposit on a £200 giant sandwich is..."   **£50**

"50% of the teachers in my school come..."   **8**

"It's normally £3.50 for a pair of monkeys..."   **35p**

Page 68 — Making Decisions

"Harry charges £5 an hour to lay bricks..."   **1200**

"Harry loses the contest to Ray, who can..."   **60 more**

"Harry and Ray work together to build..."   **11**

"The Cone has 1485 bricks. How long..."   **2 hrs 15 mins**

"41.5 × 22 = 913"
    Anything suitable, e.g. I can hold 11 mice in each hand. If
    each mouse weighs 41.5 grams, that's 913 grams in total.

"Fill in the gap in these sums: is it +, –, × or ÷?"
    =   **+**   **=**
    ×   **÷**   **×**

Page 69 — Checking Results

"Round these numbers to find an approximate answer..."
    ...500 + 500 which is 1000.
    ...30 × 20 which is 600.
    ...900 - 400 which is 500.
    ...800 ÷ 40 which is 20.

"Use the rules to say if the answers to these questions are..."
290 – 182 is **even**   863 – 236 is **odd**   909 – 281 is **even**
715 – 326 is **odd**   643 – 279 is **even**   889 – 464 is **odd**

142 + 556 is **even**   517 + 233 is **even**   316 + 349 is **even**
297 + 423 is **even**   726+ 511 is **odd**   206 + 884 is **even**
97 + 113 + 327 is **odd**

Page 70 — Square Numbers

"What is 1 squared?"   **1**

"Is 20 a square number?" **No**

"What's 5 squared?"   **25**

"What is the square of 3?" **9**

"Work out 4^2"   **16**   "Work out 5^2" **25**

"What's another way to write "3 squared"?" $\mathbf{3^2}$

"Fill these in."
Clockwise from top left: $1^2 = \mathbf{1}$, $2^2 = 4$, $10^2 = \mathbf{100}$,
$\mathbf{5^2} = 25$, $4^2 = \mathbf{16}$, $3^2 = \mathbf{9}$, $6^2 = 36$

Page 71 — Square Numbers

"What is 6^2?"   **36**

"What number multiplied by itself gives 64?"   **8**

"Is 52 a square number?" **No**

"What is the area of a square whose sides..."   **49**

"Write out all the square numbers up to 100."
    1, 4, 16, 25, 36, 49, 64, 81, 100

Page 72 — Spot the Divisible Number

"Is 72 divisible by 10?"
    No

"Does 10 go into 7540?"
    Yes

"Can 600 be divided by 100?"
    Yes

"Does 100 go into 607?"
    No

"Can 45 be shared between 5?"
    Yes

"Does 5 go into 385?"
   Yes

"Can 133 be divided by 2?"
   No

"Is 8836 divisible by 2?"
   Yes

"Will 108 divide by 4?"
   Yes

"Will 3812 divide by 4?"
   Yes

"Will 4646 divide by 4?"
   No

Page 73 — Reasoning About Numbers

"The perimeter of a rectangle is..."
   Any suitable to show it is **true**

"If you swap 2 numbers round in a subtraction sum..."
   Any suitable, e.g. $5 - 3 = 2$, but $3 - 5 = -2$

"The angles in a triangle always add up to 180°."
   Any suitable to show it's **true**

"The sum of two odd numbers..."
   Any suitable, e.g. $3 + 5 = 8$, which is **even**.
   Full Statement: **The sum of two odd numbers is even.**

Page 74 — Reasoning About Numbers

"My machine takes a number, doubles it and then..."
   3, 4, 6, 10, 18

"Describe a way to calculate the perimeter of a rectangle."
Any suitable, e.g. Add the length of one of the long sides to
the length of one of the short sides, and double the answer.

"Tony is jumping. He jumps over 1, then 2, then 4, then..."
   Any suitable, e.g.
   He starts with 1, and then doubles it each time.

Index

Index